Instructor's Guide
To Accompany
GEOMETRY
FOR TEACHERS
Second Edition

Instructor's Guide
To Accompany
GEOMETRY
FOR TEACHERS
Second Edition

C. Patrick Collier
University of Wisconsin, Oshkosh

Waveland Press, Inc.
Prospect Heights, Illinois

For information about this guide or the accompanying text, please write or call:

Waveland Press, Inc.
P.O. Box 400
Prospect Heights, Illinois 60070
(312) 634-0081

Contents

GENERAL INFORMATION AND SUGGESTIONS

Notes on Part 1: Informal Geometry and Topology.

The first eight chapters are organized under the heading "Informal Geometry and Topology". The term "informal" refers to the manner in which subject matter is treated. It is informal in the sense that there is no formal logical sequence of definitions and theorems. The material is not developed in a manner that would satisfy a rigorous logical standard. The purpose is to develop insight and tools for organizing geometric ideas. Proof of theorems is not a goal.

The topology content is primarily in the first three chapters. The idea of a curve is basic to topology and is introduced first. Separation is also a topic basic to topology. It seems to be one of the more difficult topics for some students. The idea of separation extends to several other topics in this part of the text so students do not have to learn it all in chapter 2. They will separate a line in chapter 4, separate a plane in chapter 6 and separate space in chapter 8. The third topological idea is that of network and is an extension of the idea of a curve.

The topological ideas are important for several reasons. One reason is that some understanding of topology is essential to understanding how children's ideas about space develop. Piaget says that topological ideas develop before Euclidean ideas. How can a teacher understand and appreciate this developmental principle without knowing a few topological ideas? The teacher who deals with children in the early stages of development needs some exposure to topological ideas in order to understand the development of children and as an aid in diagnosing learning difficulties. The teacher who deals with children in their latter stages of development will need exposure to topological ideas because he/she is likely to be called upon to teach some of these ideas to students.

The idea of packing (not a topological idea) is introduced in four chapters, chapter 4 through 8. Chapter 4 deals with packing on a line, chapters 5 and 6 deal with packing in a plane, chapter 8 deals with packing in space. Packing is an essential prerequisite to the concept of measurement. To measure length, a unit is chosen and repeated, or packed, and then the repetitions are counted. Packing is similarly related to measuring area and volume.

The traditional vocabulary associated with lines and planes is introduced in chapters 4, 5 and 6. While chapters 7 and 8 deal specifically with three dimensional space, some space geometry is included in other chapters. For example, curves and networks are considered as space figures as well as plane figures. Also planes are related to each other as space objects. Euler's theorem can be developed in two different settings, chapter 3 on networks in a plane and in chapter 7 on polyhedra in space.

Students have generally had more formal experience with plane geometry than with space geometry. For this reason (among others) they will have more difficulty with three dimensional space perception than with two dimensional plane perception. It may be more important to make use of physical models when dealing with space. Even helping some students to draw a picture of a cube may be time well spent.

Chapter 8 is perhaps more formal than the other topics in this part of the text and is the easiest to eliminate. It may be unwise, however, to reduce or eliminate experiences with space geometry because this is a topic that most students need more experience with. Chapter 2 also introduces an idea in a fairly formal way but this idea is applied in latter chapters. If chapter 2 were slighted perhaps more time would have to be spent on other topics to get the related ides developed properly. Chapter 3 is an extension of chapter 1 and some teachers have found they can eliminate it. This does reduce the impact and emphasis on topology and you also lose the relationship between networks and polyhedra. In summary, for the unsophisticated student most of this unit should be considered high priority.

Notes on Part 2: Motion Geometry
Chapters 9 and 10 are preliminary to the main ideas in this part of the text. Chapter 9 defines the notion of congruence and chapter 10 gives students a chance to deal with congruence on an intuitive basis. Chapter 10 also introduces many figures which are used repeatedly in the rest of the text.

Chapters 11, 12, 13 and 14 comprise the substance of motion geometry. The elementary school notions of flip, turn and slide are related to the reflection, rotation and translation congruences. Chapter 14 gets into the idea of combining two or more motions in succession. The final two chapters in this part of the text examine invariance patterns.

Each of the tree fundamental motions is developed so that students should be able to duplicate a given move using tracing paper. It is a good idea to watch students actually perform the tracings to insure that they are able to follow the directions correctly. If they cannot follow the directions they cannot build an experience base for the more sophisticated ideas that follow. Minimally students should be able to recognize when figures are congruent in one of the three special ways and they should be able to recognize when a figure is invariant for some motion.

Students have used the term "line of symmetry" so they do not have major problems with reflections. Most students can visualize reflections in vertical or horizontal lines but experience difficulty in visualizing reflections in diagonal lines. Students have more difficulty with rotation invariance and a great deal of difficulty with translation invariance. The latter difficulty is probably associated with the fact that students do not conceptualize unbounded figures as easily as they do bounded figures. To overcome this difficulty teachers can accept as a replacement idea the notion of a figure formed by translation images which are finite in number.

The notion of congruence should be seen as an important one for elementary teachers to have. Those who teach children at lower levels of development may not teach about congruence in a formal way but the notion is a cornerstone of their "perceptual skills curriculum." Many of the activities of these children is distinguishing likes and differences. "Likes" are really congruences. Chapters 9 and 10 are helpful in understanding the perceptual skills curriculum. Understanding the content of chapters 9 and 10 will be an aid to recognizing perceptual difficulties that the teachers and students have.

Chapter 9 is essential to the rest of the unit. Chapter 10 provides valuable experience with congruence at an intuitive level before proceeding to motion geometry. Polyominoes and polycubes can be related to the idea of a tangram in chapter 17. Chapters 11 through 14 should be considered essential. Topics 15 and 16 can be considered optional. If they are skipped consideration should be given to introducing the idea of congruence modulo an integer because this notion is needed to measure anglesize using a coordinate circle.

Notes on Part 3: Metric Geometry

The first chapter in this part of the text develops a prerequisite to measurement, the notion of conservation. The tangram principle is an extension of earlier work with packing and on work with polyominoes and polycubes. Chapters 18, 19, 20 and 21 are concerned with the four basic measurements of geometric objects: length, anglesize, area and volume. Chapters 22 and 23 are not necessarily metric topics but are included here because the definition of similarity used the idea of length. The notion of similarity also helps to relate length, area and volume measures of solids to one another. Central similarity provides a means for testing plane objects to see if they are similar. This provides an opportunity for distinguishing between exact measurement and approximation. It also provides a means for developing the method for finding the volume of a pyramid and for like objects. Chapter 24 is an important topic in understanding measurement in general.

Ideas that relate to measurement have been in the curriculum of the elementary school for a long time. They are not as new as topology or motion geometry. However, the amount of time devoted to this topic is not substantial. There is recent indication that this topic is not developed very well in many elementary schools.

Often the idea of measurement is associated with the memorization of a formula. This text emphasizes the importance of a strong foundation starting with conservation tasks and ending with measures which are derived by computation. Formulas come at the end of the development and are seen as relations that should be reconstructed as needed rather than memorized.

The first five chapters of this part of the text form a sequence which should have high priority. The fifth topic in chapter 21 deals with measuring solids and like other topics dealing with solids is fairly difficult for students. If a good job is done on chapters 17 through 21 the essentials of metric geometry would be learned.

Any of the last three topics could be eliminated without adverse effect on other topics. If chapter 22 is covered then you should also do

the first two sections in chapter 23. Students would then have a
method for testing for similarity that seems to be easier for them
to use than other methods.

Notes on Language
The text is written in an informal rather than a rigorous style.
Consequently the undefined terms are not explicitly stated and no
effort is made to define each term precisely in terms of undefined
terms and previously defined terms. The reading material is to suggest
a working definition of a term in most cases. In order to compensate
for this lack of explicitness a glossary and index is included at the
end of the text (p 301-308). The definitions in the glossary are
more explicit and more carefully formed. However even here there is
no attempt to systemmatize the language.

The text was written with the belief that rigorous definitions, if they
are to come, must necessarily follow a working period in which more
tentative definitions are used. The choice here has been to be precise
when it appears that the intended audience can understand and apply it
and to be imprecise when it might lead to a better understanding.

There are very few words that students will need to memorize. Students
should exhibit their understanding (or lack of it) by recognizing and
producing examples and counterexamples. They should be using the terms
in class when they discuss exercises, constructions or problems. When
they can use the terms properly then they can understand that the
definitions in the glossary make sense.

Notes on Problem Solving
There are six to eight problems at the end of each chapter. These problems
are often open ended situations that call for students to construct
something or to find some pattern or relation. Students may or may not
like to be exposed to problems. In studying the attitudes of students
who used the first edition of the text I found that students agreed
with abstract statements about problem solving and discovery situations.
In practice their attitude about searching and discovering is neutral
or even negative when it comes to their own involvement. Students
indicated strong agreement with "course should be structured to get
students actively involved" and fairly strong agreement with "students
prefer the opportunity to discover rather than being told". They agree
only slightly with requiring coursework that involves discovering and
experimenting and problem solving. They are neutral with regard to
the use of problems as an activity in this course. Problem solving is
seen as a valuable experience for others but too frustrating for themselves.

This suggests that the handling of the problems is the critical issue
in teaching this course. Too much emphasis on problems leads to
frustrated students who feel that they are spending too much time and
not finding solutions. Too little emphasis on problems denies students
an opportunity to use skills in a more natural setting and reinforces the
attitude that mathematics is routine and symbol pushing and memorizing
and not exploring and investigating and problem solving.

Students with poorer backgrounds in mathematics encounter greater frustration in problem solving. When dealing with these students it is important not to assign too many problems. I usually expect that each student will submit a written or oral report on one problem in every second chapter we cover. If I cover 24 chapters I will collect 12 written reports on problems. The problem assignments should be considered as an opportunity to discuss general problem solving strategies and attitudes. Written work should be evaluated for strategy and for use of language as well as for a specific solution. Some problem solving experience is valuable even when a solution is not found. In some cases the student is practicing a skill, in other cases the student may be generating examples of a particular concept. It is important to give recognition to students who demonstrate basic skill proficiency in written problem assignments even when they have not solved the problem.

I ask that students write more than a solution to a problem. I expect them to tell what their strategy or thought process was. Some students show recognition of the heuristics, guess and check, divide the task into smaller tasks, try to find a related but simpler problem and try to explain how I'd know it was solved. They can demonstrate that they have some understanding of the problem solving process even when they cannot apply the process successfully in a particular situation.

I have tried weighting the problem solving experiences with different weights and have settled on 1/5 or 1/6 as reasonable. This seems to provide enough incentive to get honest attempts but not so much that it discourages students.

Notes on Answers
The rest of this guide is devoted to answers to exercises, constructions and problems. The answers to the constructions should be taken as samples. In most cases there are many answers and just one or two are provided. The exercises were worked carefully and then checked. However it is still possible that errors exist. Questions about solutions or any correspondence regarding the text is welcome. Contact the author c/o Mathematics Department, University of Wisconsin-Oshkosh 54901.

CHAPTER 1

1. B, C, M, P, Q, S, W, 2, 4, 6, 8 are plane curves.
2. A, B, C are curves. D is not traceable, E is not connected.
3. C, D and J are closed, rest are open. C, G and J are simple.
4. (A) 12; (B) 8; (C) 12; (D) 4; (E) 4 .
5. (A) 6; (B) 8; (C) 4; (D) 8; (E) 8 .
6. (A) 9; (B) 10; (C) 1; (D) 3; (E) 5; (F) 18; (G) 8; (H) 5 .
7. (A) 7; (B) 4; (C) 4; (D) 1; (E) 15 .
8. D is not equivalent because first curve is open and second is closed.
    E is not equivalent because first figure is a curve, second is not.
    H is not equivalent because the loops are pieced together differently
    (first has three loops meeting at one point, the other does not)
9. There are really four classes rather than five. A, C, F, H are one
    class; B,G other; D, I a third and E, J a fourth. If five classes
    are created A, C, F, H can be partitioned into two classes arbitrarily.

CHAPTER 2

1. Figures B, C, E and G are not connected. B has three components,
    C has two components, E has two components, G has five components.
2. (A) none; (B) each of the six points of order four; (C) none;
    (D) any of the infinitely many points not on a loop; (E) each of the
    six points of order four or any of the infinitely many points of the
    two "tails" (except the endpoints); (F) none; (G) two points of order
    eight (common point for four loops); (H) one point; (I) every point
    except the seven "end" points; (J) every point except the eight "end"
    points; (K) any of the infinitely many points which connect left
    "triangle" to next crossing point; (L) any point on one of the six
    segments to the left or right of the "square" (except for six endpoints).
3. (B) two components for each separation; (D) points on arcs separate
    into two components, points of order four separate into three components;
    (E) one separating point creates three components, the others create
    two; (G) each of the two separating points creates three components;
    (H) only separating point creates two components; (I) five separating
    points have three components, others have two; (J) one separating
    point creates four components, four separating points create three
    components, all others have two components; (K) all separating points
    have two components; (L) two separating points have four components,
    all others have two components.
4. A and C separate the plane. They are simple closed curves.
5. Except for A and B in first figure a separating arc must contain some
    boundary point of the given figure other than A or B, P or Q.
6. Eight triples: RYW, UXZ, TWY, SXZ, YRT, ZSU, WRT, XSU.
7. Four triples: ADF, AGE, CGE, BGE.
8. Six triples: Q,P,R ; Q,P,S ; Q,P,T ; S,P,T ; S,Q,T ; S,R,T ;
    Note that Q and S are separating points.

CHAPTER 3

1. B, C and G are networks. A, D, E and H are not connected, F has two arcs
    intersecting in a point not a vertex.

2. (A) five arcs, five vertices; (B) seven arcs, six vertices; (C) one arc, two vertices; (D) five arcs, four vertices.
3. (A) need four vertices; (B) need four vertices; (C) need four vertices; (D) need five vertices; (E) need two vertices.
4. (A) A-2, B-3, C-3, D-5, E-3, F-2 four odd and two even; (B) G-1, H-3, I-2, J-3, K-2, L-3 four odd and two even; (C) M-4, N-4, P-6, O-4, Q-6 none odd and five even; (D) R-2, S-2, T-3, U-3, W-2, X-3 four odd and two even.
5. (A) none; (B) one separating vertex, two components; (C) one separating vertex, three components; (D) three separating vertices, each has two components; (E) two separating vertices, one has three components, the other has two; (F) two separating vertices, one has four components, the other has three; (G) same as E; (H) one separating vertex, four components; (I) four separating vertices, three have two components, one has three; (J) two separating vertices, each has two components.
6. (A) none; (B) none; (C) two; (D) two; (E) three; (F) six; (G) three; (H) three; (I) six; (J) two.
7. (A)   (B)   (C)   (D)

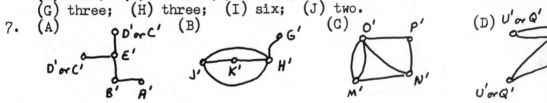

8. (A) first network has one vertex of order 4, second has two vertices of order 4; (B) first network has ten arcs, second has nine; (C) in first network there are seven arcs, second has eight; (D) in first network the two vertices of order two are connected directly to the same vertex, in the second they are not.
9. A and G, B and E, C and J, D and I, F and H.

CHAPTER 4

1. (A) one; (B) three; (C) four; (D) four.
2. (A) three; (B) three; (C) six; (D) six.
3. (A)-(H) are dense. (I)-(L) are finite so they cannot be dense.
4. (A) open segment; (B) half-line; (C) half-line; (D) line; (E) point; (F) half-line; (G) ray; (H) line; (I) half-line; (J) half-line; (K) line; (L) empty.
5. (A)   (B)   (C) empty;

(D)   (E) line; (F) single point, 0

(G)   (H)

6. (A) $\{x \mid x \leq -1\} \cup \{x \mid x \geq 2\}$; (B) $\{x \mid 1 \leq x \leq 3\} \cup \{x \mid 5 \leq x \leq 7\}$; (C) $\{x \mid x > -2\} \cap \{x \mid x \leq 3\}$; (D) $\{x \mid x = 5\}$; (E) $\{x \mid x \leq 7\}$; (F) $\{x \mid x$ is real$\}$ or $\{x \mid x > 1\} \cup \{x \mid x < 3\}$; (G) $\{x \mid x < -7\} \cup \{x \mid x > -3\}$; (H) $\{x \mid x > 6\} \cap \{x \mid x < 10\}$.
7. (A) eleven; (B) eleven; (C) fifteen; (D) fifteen.

8. (A) AB, AF, AG, BF, BG, FG;   (B) AB, AC, AD, BC, BD, CD;
   (C) AF, AG, AD, FG, FD, GD;   (D) AE, AF, AH, EF, EH, FH.
9. (A) KL = LM = KM, KN, LN, MN;   (B) KM, KP, KQ, MP, MQ, PQ;
   (C) PQ = QR = PR, QR, OQ, OP, MP, MQ, MR, OM;
   (D) OQ, ON, OL, OK, QN, QL, QK, NL, NK, LK.

CHAPTER 5

1. B, C, G, H, I and M are not polygons because they are not simple
   closed curves; F, J and K not polygons because not union of segments.
2. (A) six; (B) six; (C) thirteen; (D) ten; (E) six.
3. (A) equilateral; (B) equilateral; (C) regular; (D) equilateral;
   (E) equilateral; (F) regular; (G) equilateral; (H) equiangular;
   (I) equiangular; (J) equiangular; (K) equilateral; (L) equiangular.
4. See packing patterns on next page, page 9.
5. (A) 12; (B) 30; (C) 11; (D) 10; (E) 9; (F) 9; (G) 11, (H) 16.
6. A, D and G are convex.
7. (A) 4; (B) 10; (C) 18; (D) 11; (E) 8; (F) 7; (G) 3; (H) 10.
8. (A) 3; (B) 4; (C) 22; (D) 0; (E) 3; (F) 3; (G) 3; (H) 0.

CHAPTER 6

1. A, B, F and H separate the plane. A, B and F separate into two
   components, H separates into four components.
2. (A) open half-plane and closed half-plane; (B) closed angular region
   and open angular region; (C) both have triangular boundaries, one is
   open the other closed; one is bounded the other unbounded; (D) both
   triangular regions with triangular holes; in one the boundary of the
   hole is included, in the other it is not included.
3. Those bounded are E, F, G, I, K, M, N. Cannot decide in C, J or L.
4. B, C and E are bounded.
5. See packing patterns on next page, page 10.
6. Not all angular regions pack. If an angular region packs then exactly
   n copies must pack around a point for n ≥ 3. So the anglesize must be
   360/n degrees if the region is to pack.
7. B, E and G do not pack. See packing patterns on next page, page 10.
8. There are six segments and every pair is a parallel pair. Rays AB,
   BC and CD are mutually parallel; Rays DC, CB and BA are mutually
   parallel.
9. KL & KM, LM & KM, KL & LM, KL & PQ, LM & PQ, KM & PQ, KP & LQ,
   AND PL & QM are pairs of parallel segments. Pairs of parallel rays
   are: KL & LM, KL & PQ, LM & PQ, IK & ML, IK & QP, ML & QP,
   PK & QL, KP & LQ, PL & QM, LP & MQ.
10. Four point sets: ABHE, DCGF, BCGH, EFGH, EFDA, ADBC, ADHG, BEFC,
    AFBG, DEHC, ACEG, DBHF. Three point sets: AFC, BDG, HCF, EDG,
    DBE, CHA, GEB, FAH,
11. Five point planes: ABCDE. Four point planes: CDGF, BEFG, AEDF,
    ABCG, ABCF, AEDG. Three point planes: AFG, ECG, BDF

CHAPTER 5. Exercise 4.

(A)

(B)
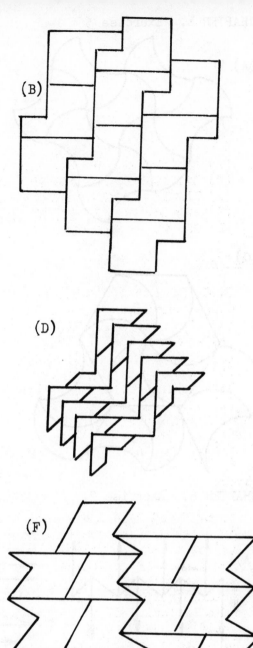

(C)
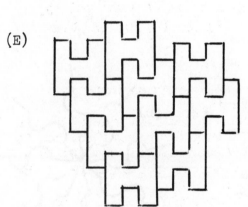

(D)

(E)

(F)
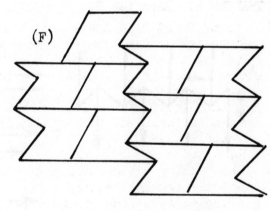

(G)
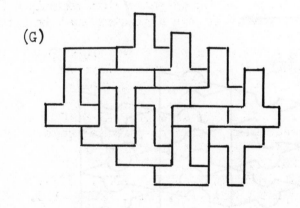

(H)
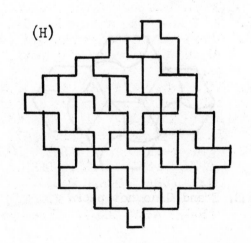

9.

CHAPTER 6. Exercise 5

(A)

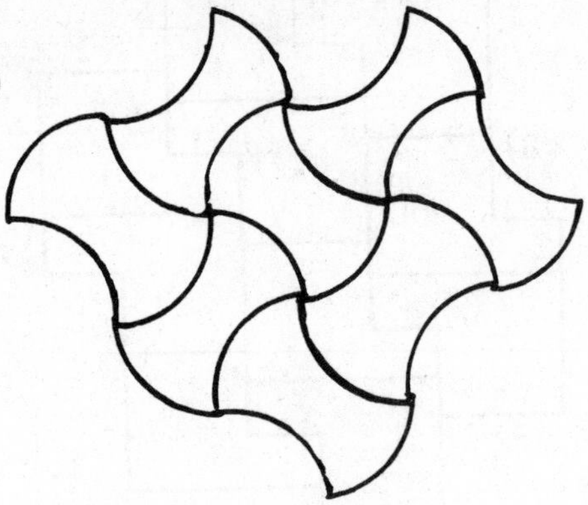

(B)

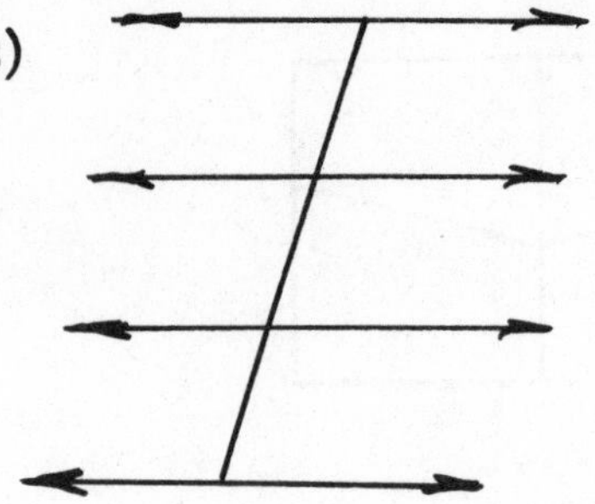

(C)

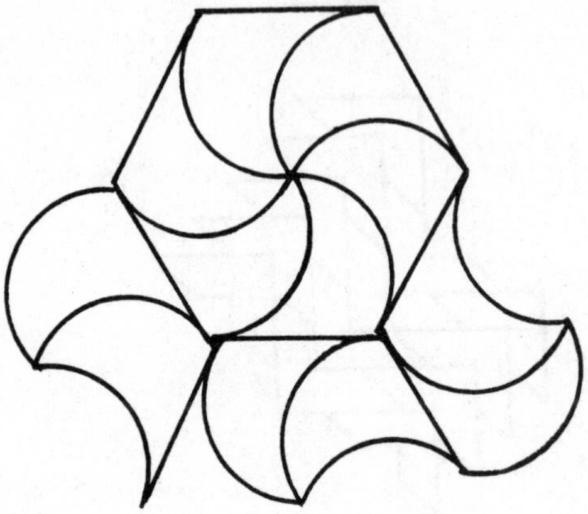

(E)

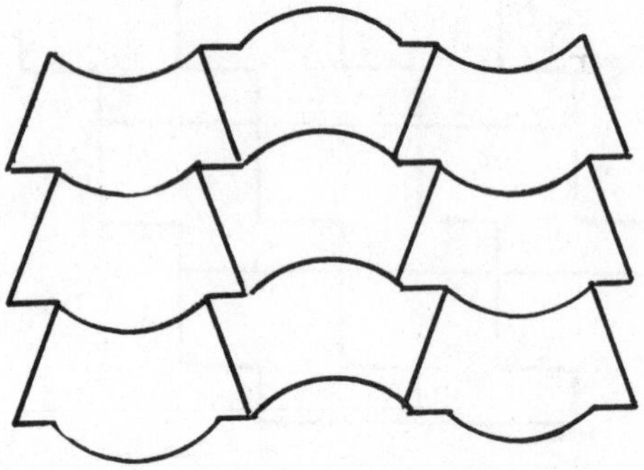

CHAPTER 6. Exercise 7.

(A)

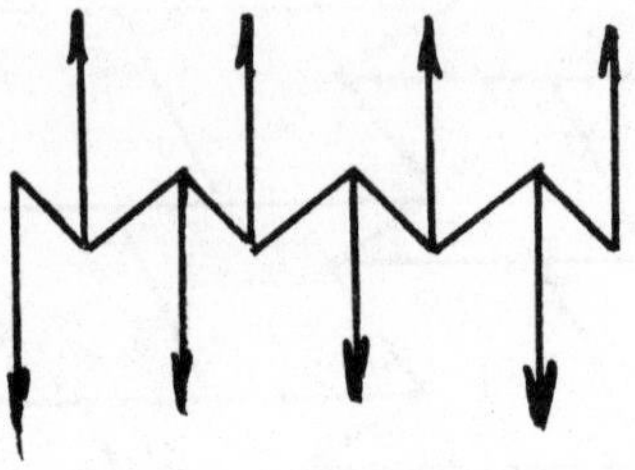

(C)

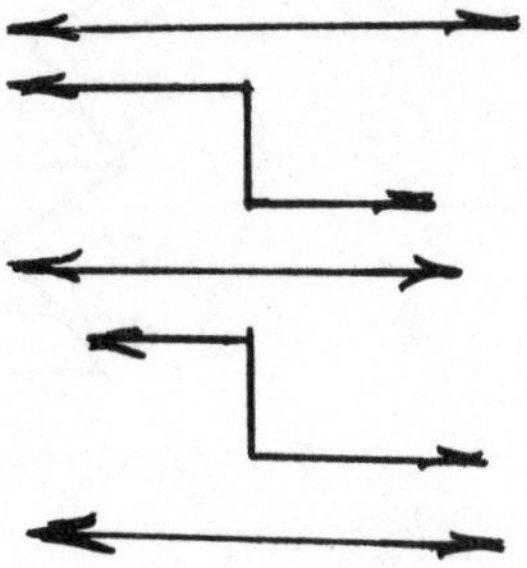

(D)

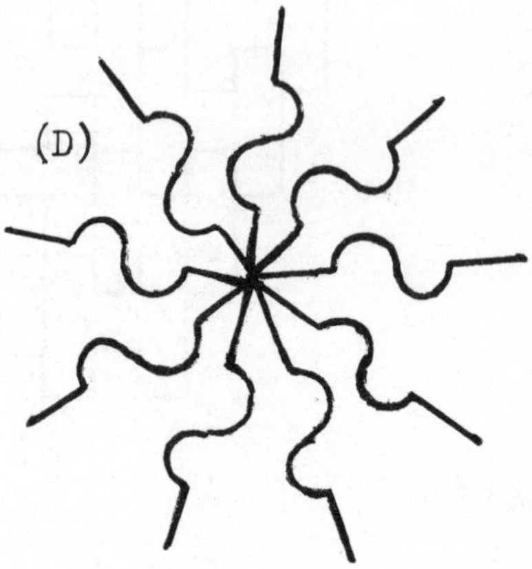

(F)

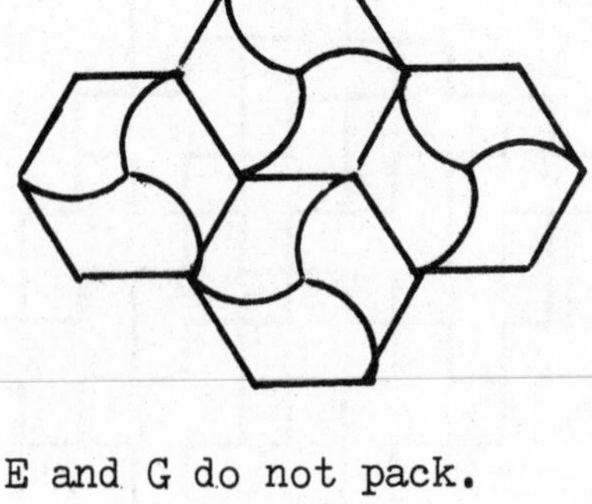

(H)

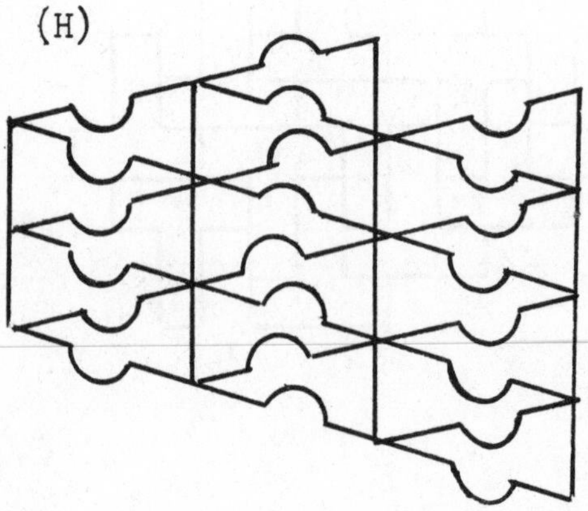

B, E and G do not pack.

CHAPTER 7

1. G, J, M and O are not polyhedra because none is the union of plane surfaces.
2. R is the only pyramid.
3. A is the only prism.
4. (A) V = 20, E = 30, F = 12; (B) V = 22, E = 36, F = 16; (C) V = 19, E = 30, F = 13; (D) V = 17, E = 27, F = 12; (E) V = 22, E = 34, F = 14; (F) V = 16, E = 24, F = 10; (G) not a polyhedron; (H) V = 10, E = 15, F = 7; (I) V = 13, E = 22, F = 11; (J) not a polyhedron; (K) V = 12, E = 20, F = 10; (L) V = 9, E = 16, F = 9; (M) not a polyhedron; (N) V = 12, E = 20, F = 10; (O) not a polyhedron; (P) V = 14, E = 26, F = 14; (Q) V = 11, E = 20, F = 11 (a visible edge is missing in first printing) (R) V = 5, E = 8, F = 5; (S) V = 8, E = 12, F = 6; (T) V = 7, E = 11, F = 6.
5. There are no regular polyhedra in (A)–(T).
6. A, B, D and E are polyhedra. (A) V = 8, E = 12, F = 6; (B) V = 12, E = 18, F = 8; (D) V = 5, E = 8, F = 5; (E) V = 8, E = 12, F = 6. See sketches below.

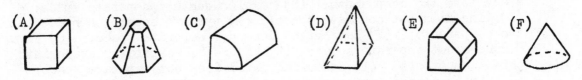

(A) (B) (C) (D) (E) (F)

7.

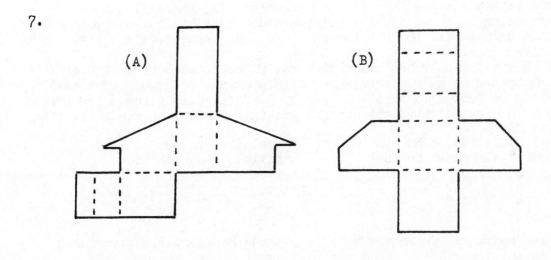

(A) (B)

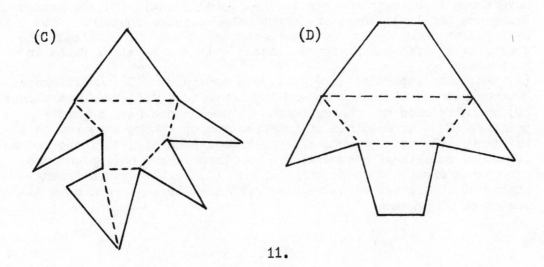

(C) (D)

CHAPTER 8.

1. Plane curves are A, B, G and I. Space curves are C, D, E, F, H, J. Simple curves are A, B, C, D, I, J. Open curves are A, D, E, H, J.

2. (A) All horizontal and vertical cross sections are circular regions; (B) Horizontal cross sections are circular regions, vertical cross section is triangular region or a parabolic region; (C) Horizontal cross sections are circular regions, vertical cross sections are rectangular regions; (D) Horizontal cross sections are annular regions, vertical cross sections are disjoint circular regions or disjoint elliptical regions or another single region.

3. (A) Plane separates space into two half-spaces; (B) cylinder separates space into two components; (C) circle does not separate space; (D) line does not separate space; (E) pyramid separates space into two components; (F) half plane does not separate space; (G) Figure 8.2 does not separate space; (H) Figure 8.7 separates space into three components; (I) spherical solid does not separate space; (J) simple closed curve does not separate space; (K) two intersecting planes separate space into four components; (L) three planes intersecting in three lines separates space into six components; (M) two half planes which intersect in a line separate space into two components.

4. A, B, E are prisms whose bases pack the plane. Two copies of C or D can be packed to make a cube which does pack space. Two copies of F or H can be packed to make a 2 by 2 by 3 rectangular prism which packs space. G does not have the spacial packing property unless reflection copies are used.

5.

	relative to MN			relative to OP		
	parallel	skew	neither	parallel	skew	neither
A)	6	7	5	6	8	4
B)	6	7	5	6	7	5
C)	4	8	6	4	8	6
D)	4	8	6	4	8	6

6. (A) two hexagonal faces are parallel, three horizontal square faces are mutually parallel, three vertical square faces are mutually parallel; (B) there are three classes of parallel faces, two classes have three faces each one has two hexagonal faces; (C) the hexagonal bases are parallel, there are three other classes containing two rectangular faces each; (D) the hexagonal bases are parallel, the remaining six faces form three classes with two parallel faces in each class.

7. (A) yes, both separate; (B) yes, both separate; (C) no difference between ray and line on a sphere but there is a difference in plane; (D) no half-lines on spheres because lines do not have separating points; (E) 1 or 2 points of intersection on sphere compared to 1 in plane; (F) two segments can separate a sphere; (G) there are no unbounded subsets of a sphere; (H) hemisphere and half-plane are components created by separating line; (I) regular plane triangle has angles of 60 degrees each, regular spherical triangle can have all angles of 90 degrees.

CHAPTER 9

1. Congruent pairs: AD, BI, CF, EH, GJ, KL.
2. Answer yes for A, C, D, F, G, I, J.
3. (A)   (B)   (C)   (D)

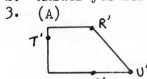 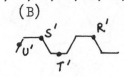 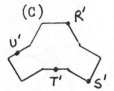 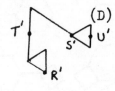

4. (A) No, eg. XY≠KL; (B) Yes; (C) No, eg XY≠LK; (D) Yes;
   (E) No, eg XY≠NL; (F) Yes; (G) No, eg TU≠OQ; (H) No, eg TV≠RP;
   (I) No, eg TU≠QO; (J) Yes; (K) No, eg BC≠FJ; (L) No, eg DE≠IF;
   (M) Yes.
5. (A) one; (B) two; (C) two; (D) two; (E) two; (F) two; (G) four.
   (H) two; (I) infinitely many; (J) two; (K) four; (L) one.
6. A, C, G are all congruent; D, J, H are all congruent; E, F, I are
   all congruent.
7.   (A)   (B)   (C)   (D)

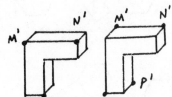 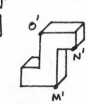 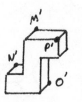 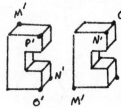  

CHAPTER 10

1. (A) there are six; (B) there are nine; (C) there are five;
   (D) there are six; (E) there are eleven.
2. (A) there are six; (B) there are four; (C) there are seven;
   (D) there is one; (E) there are two.
3. (A) four quadrominoes, one pentomino; (B) one quadromino, one
   pentomino; (C) four quadrominoes, five pentominoes; (D) five
   quadrominoes, two pentominoes; (E) four quadrominoes, four pentominoes.
4. (A) two pentiamonds, one hexiamond; (B) two pentiamonds, two
   hexiamonds; (C) two pentiamonds, one hexiamond; (D) three pentiamonds,
   two hexiamonds; (E) four pentiamonds, two hexiamonds.
5. (A) there are five; (B) there are thirty-two; (C) there are fifteen;
   (D) there are eleven; (E) there are seven. (See sketch page 14,15)
   for sketches of different figures).
6. (A) four quadracubes, one pentacube; (B) two quadracubes, one pentacube;
   (C) four quadracubes, two pentacubes; (D) two quadracubes, three
   pentacubes; (E) two quadracubes, one pentacube; (F) two quadracubes,
   one pentacube; (G) four quadracubes, three pentacubes; (H) two
   quadracubes, two pentacubes.

CHAPTER 10. Exercise 5

(A)

(B)
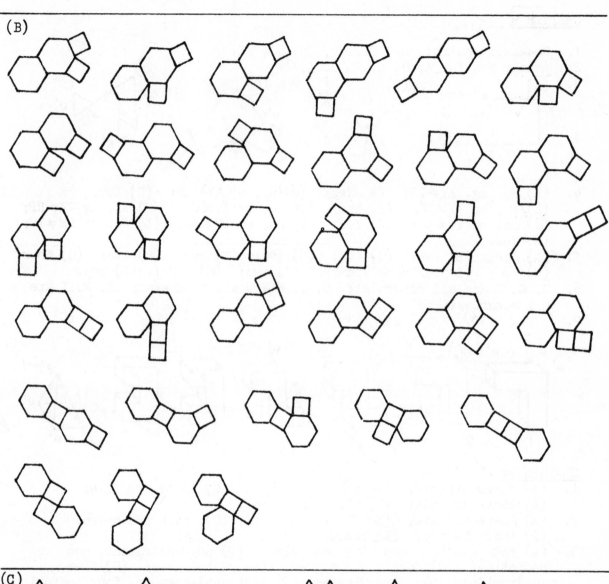

(C)
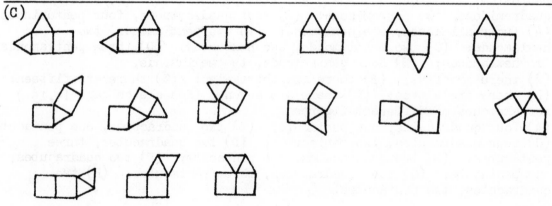

CHAPTER 10. Exercise 5.
(D)

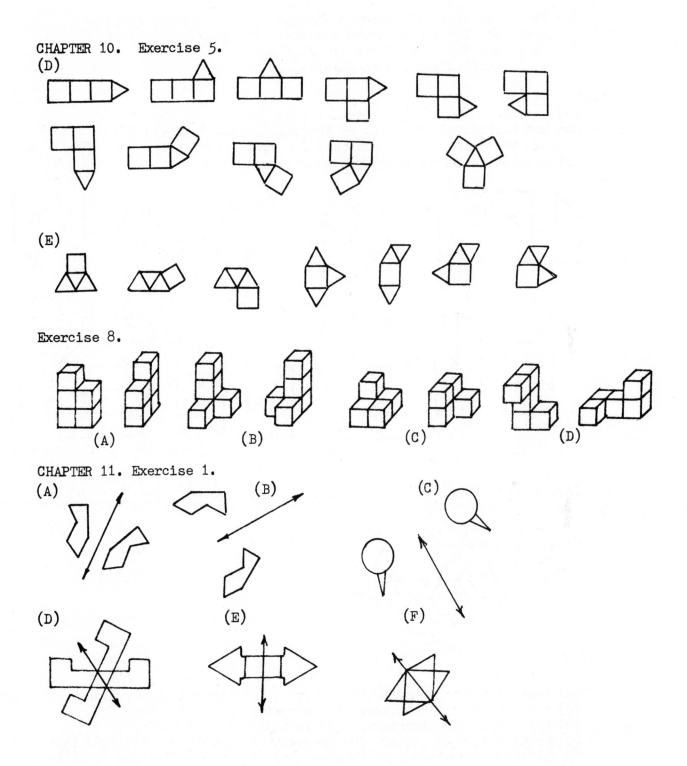

(E)

Exercise 8.

(A)   (B)   (C)   (D)

CHAPTER 11. Exercise 1.
(A)   (B)   (C)

(D)   (E)   (F)

7. (A) there are six; (B) there are eight; (C) there are fourteen;
   (D) there are four; (E) there are ten; (F) there are eleven;
   (G) there are ten; (H) there are eighteen.
8. For some examples see sketch page 15.

CHAPTER 11
1. See the sketch page for figures. (pg 15)
2. Can use horizontal, vertical or diagonal (slope 1 or -1) lines
   through the center of the geoboard for reflection lines.
3. Orientation reversing correspondences are A, C, D.
4.

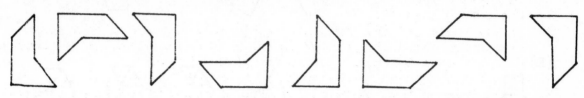

5.

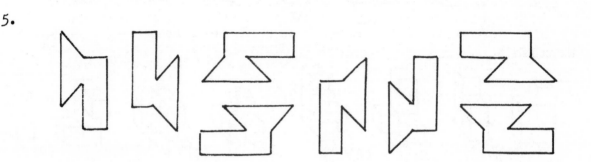

6. (A) No; (B) Yes; (C) No; (D) No; (E) No; (F) No; (G) No; (H) Yes.
7.

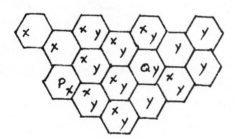

8. (A) invariant in one horizontal line; (B) invariant in two lines;
   (C) not reflection invariant; (D) invariant in four lines;
   (E) not reflection invariant; (F) invariant in two lines;
   (G) invariant in one line; (H) invariant in one line; (I) invariant
   in one line; (J) invariant in one line; (K) not reflection invariant;
   (L) not reflection invariant.

9. (A) invariant in one vertical plane; (B) invariant in two planes;
   (C) invariant in one vertical plane; (D) not reflection invariant;
   (E) invariant in three planes; (F) invariant in two planes;
   (G) not reflection invariant; (H) invariant in two planes.
10.   (A)   (B)   (C)   (D)

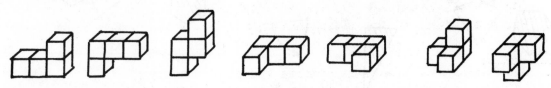

CHAPTER 12.
1. See sketch page 18.
2. See sketch page 18.
3. In all cases (A)-(H) the center geoboard point can be used as turn
   center for turns of 1/4, 1/2 and 3/4 clockwise turns. Each produces
   a figure rotation congruent to the given figure.
4. Rotation congruent pairs are A, C, D, E and G.
5. Pairs F and H from exercise 4 cannot be rotation congruent because
   one member of the pair has orientation opposite the other member
   of the pair.
6. Figures B, E, F, G, H, I, J are rotation invariant.
7. Figures B, E, F, H and J have a center of symmetry. G and I are
   rotation invariant but not for half turns so they have no center
   of symmetry.
8.   (A)   (B)   (C)   (D)   (E)

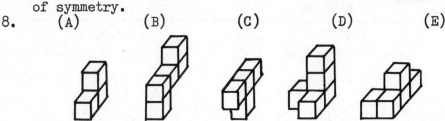

9. (A) one axis, half turns; (B) one axis, half turns; (C) not rotation
   invariant; (D) one axis, half turns; (E) not rotation invariant;
   (F) one axis, any amount of turn; (G) one axis, half turn; (H) not
   rotation invariant; (I) one axis, any amount of turn; (J) one axis
   quarter turns; four axes, half turns; (K) one axis, quarter turns;
   (L) one axis, any amount of turn; infinitely many axes, half turns.

CHAPTER 13

1. See sketch page 18.
2. (A)   (C)   (E)   (G)

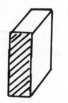   

CHAPTER 12. Exercise 1.

(A)

(B)

(C)

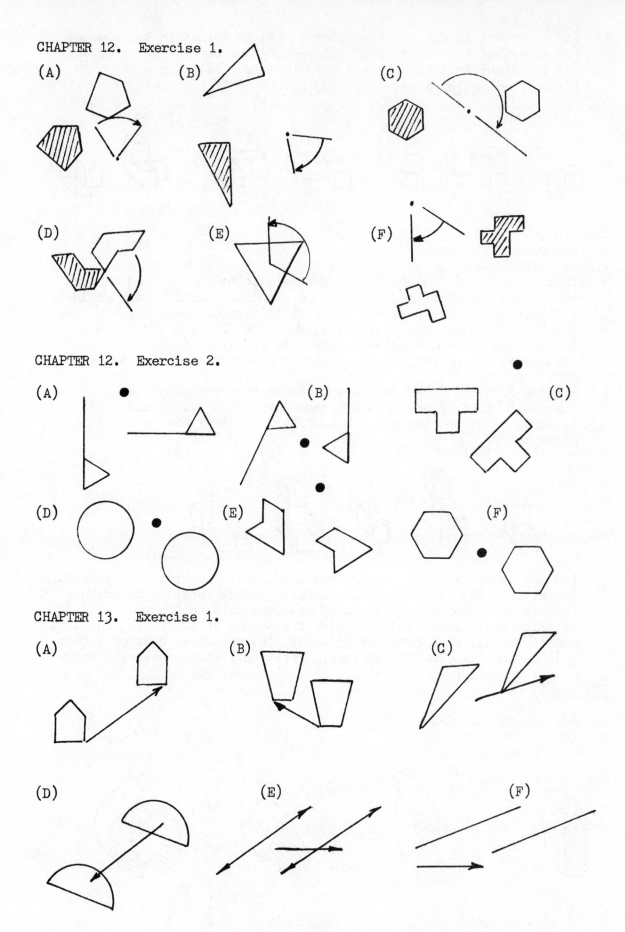

(D)

(E)

(F)

CHAPTER 12. Exercise 2.

(A)

(B)

(C)

(D)

(E)

(F)

CHAPTER 13. Exercise 1.

(A)

(B)

(C)

(D)

(E)

(F)

18.

3. Using labels from Figure 13.14 pg 154: (A) use vectors HC, HB, HM; (B) use vectors DC, DJ, DH; (C) use vectors BG, BC, BH; (D) use vectors GA, GB, GC, GF, GL.
4. translation congruent pairs are B, C, E and H.
5. pairs are: AH, BG, BL, CD, CJ, DJ, EI, GL, KM, KO, MO.
6. no pictures are provided. check responses by checking to see that all five vectors are equivalent (ie parallel and same length).
7. (A) DG; (B) KC; (C) none; (D) LO; (E) HM; (F) FE; (G) CB; (H) KG; (I) OC; (J) none; (K) KE; (L) BL.
8. translation invariant figures are: C, F, G, H, I, L, M.
9. F, G, H, I, L, M are periodic.

CHAPTER 14

1. (A) U; (B) N; (C) H; (D) E; (E) P; (F) Q; (G) C; (H) P; (I) C; (J) E; (K) M; (L) H; (M) U; (N) X; (O) I.
2. (A) Y; (B) B; (C) H; (D) K; (E) Q; (F) Q; (G) M; (H) M; (I) H; (J) off board; (K) M; (L) off board.
3. See sketch page 20.
4. See sketch page 20.
5. See sketch page 20.
6. See sketch page 26.
7. The following are sample answers. Use labels from Figure 13.14 of text. (A) JYZP; (B) FCKY; (C) not possible; (D) AFYZUTNHGB;
8. AB, AF, AG, AI, BD, BH, BJ, CF, CG, CI, DE, DG, FH, FJ, HI, IJ.
9. (A) translation; (B) rotation; (C) translation; (D) rotation; (E) rotation; (F) trivial translation or rotation; (G) none of these; (H) rotation; (I) none of these; (J) reflection.

CHAPTER 15

1. (A) R1 is one-third turn; R2 is two-thirds turn; (B) R1 is one-fourth turn; R2 is two-fourths turn; (C) R1 is one-sixth turn; R2 is two-sixths turn; (D) R1 is one-half turn; R2 not meaningful; (E) R1 is one-fourth turn; R2 is two-fourths turn; (F) R1, R2 not meaningful; (G) R1 is half-turn; R2 not meaningful; (H) R1 is one-fourth turn; R2 is two-fourths turn; (I) R1 is one-third turn; R2 is two-thirds turn; (J) R1 is one-fourth turn; R2 is two-fourths turn.

2. (A) $R_3 \circ R_4 = R_1$ so $3 +_6 4 = 1$. (B) $R_4 \circ R_2 = R_0$ so $4 +_6 2 = 0$.

(C) $R_3 \circ R_2 = R_5$ so $3 +_6 2 = 5$; (D) $R_5 \circ R_2 = R_7$ so $5 +_8 2 = 7$;

(E) $R_6 \circ R_4 = R_2$ so $6 +_8 4 = 2$; (F) $R_7 \circ R_5 = R_4$ so $7 +_8 5 = 4$;

(G) $R_6 \circ R_4 = R_1$ so $6 +_9 4 = 1$; (H) $R_3 \circ R_6 = R_2$ so $3 +_7 6 = 2$;

(I) $R_1 \circ R_1 = R_0$ so $1 +_2 1 = 0$; (J) $R_1 \circ R_1 = R_2$ so $1 +_3 1 = 2$;

(K) $R_1 \circ R_1 = R_2$ so $1 +_4 1 = 2$; (L) $R_1 \circ R_1 = R_2$ so $1 +_5 1 = 2$.

3. (A) 3, 8, 13, 18, 23; (B) 2, 5, 8, 11, 14; (C) 4, 11, 18, 25, 32; (D) 3, 7, 11, 15, 19; (E) 1, 5, 9, 13, 17; (F) 2, 7, 12, 17, 22; (G) 5, 11, 17, 23, 29; (H) 3, 10, 17, 24, 31; (I) 2, 15, 28, 41, 54; (J) 7, 24, 41, 58, 75; (K) 1, 22, 43, 64, 85; (L) 29, 64, 99, 134, 169.

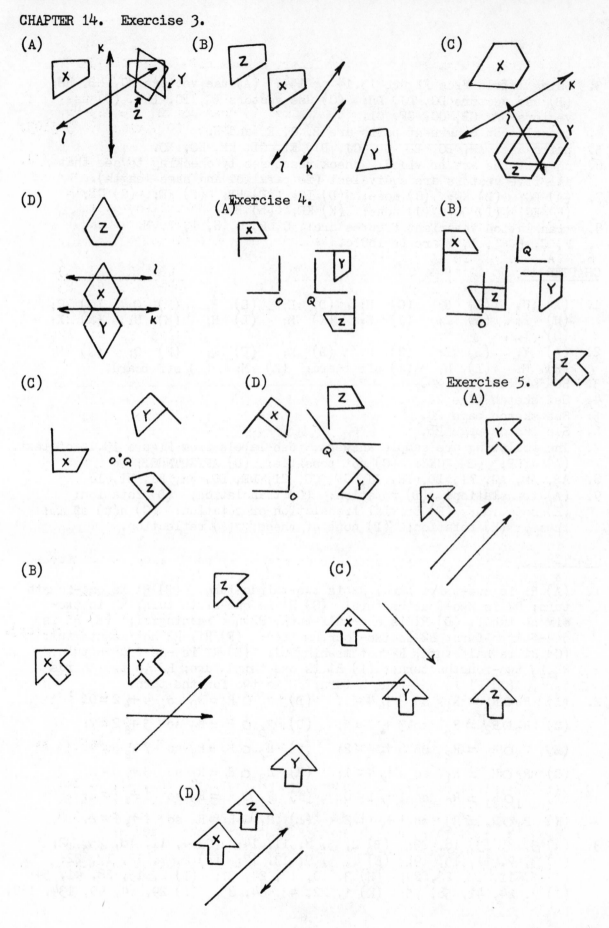

(A)

(B)

(C)

(D)

Exercise 4.

(A)

(B)

(C)

(D)

Exercise 5.

(A)

(B)

(C)

(D)

4. (A) true, 3 divides 13-7; (B) false, 2 does not divide 18-13; (C) true, 5 divides 23-8; (D) true, 7 divides 43-22; (E) false, 6 does not divide 87-50; (F) true, 7 divides 153-76; (G) false, 13 does not divide 153-76; (H) false, 13 does not divide 423-86; (I) false, 15 does not divide 423-88; (J) true, 10 divides 6423-3103.

5. A, B, C, F are possible.

6. (A) 3 (for 3/4); (B) 1 (for 1/3); (C) 2 (for 2/4); (D) 2 (for 2/5).

7. (A) two rotations, no reflections; (B) one trivial rotation, one reflection; (C) two rotations, two reflections; (D) one trivial rotation, one reflection; (E) two rotations, no reflections; (F) one trivial rotation, one reflection; (G) three rotations, three reflections; (H) two rotations, no reflections.

8. (A) see Figure 15.7, pg 176.

(B)

	RO	R1	Яk	Яl
RO	RO	R1	Яk	Яl
R1	R1	RO	Яl	Яk
Яk	Яk	Яl	RO	R1
Яl	Яl	Яk	R1	RO

(C)

	RO	R1
RO	RO	R1
R1	R1	RO

(D)

	RO	R1	R2	R3
RO	RO	R1	R2	R3
R1	R1	R2	R3	RO
R2	R2	R3	RO	R1
R3	R3	RO	R1	R2

CHAPTER 16

1. the vectors for invariant translations must all be horizontal in A, C, D, E, F. Each must be a period vector or a whole number multiple of a period vector. (See answers 2 & 3).

2. there are always two ways to label the figures because there is a choice of two directions for the positive direction. Once the origin and the positive direction is chosen there is only one way to label the other points.

3. lengths of period vectors are approximately: (A) 8 mm; (B) 13 mm; (C) 22 mm; (D) 13 mm; (E) 11 mm; (F) 10 mm.

4. A, E and G are translation invariant.

5. students should check their own responses by performing translations and checking for invariance.

6. Let T_n be translation with respect to a vector which is parallel to and n times the length of a given fixed period vector. (If n is negative then T_n has length n but direction opposite the period vector). (A) Since $T_5 \circ T_3 = T_8$ we have $3 + 5 = 8$; (B) Since $T_{-5} \circ T_3 = T_{-2}$ we have $3 + -5 = -2$; (C) Since $T_5 \circ T_{-3} = T_2$ we have $-3 + 5 = 2$; (D) Since $T_{-5} \circ T_{-3} = T_{-8}$ we have $-3 + -5 = -8$; (E) Since $T_7 \circ T_4 = T_{11}$ we have $4 + 7 = 11$; (F) Since $T_{-7} \circ T_4 = T_{-3}$ we have $4 + -7 = -3$; (G) Since $T_7 \circ T_{-4} = T_3$ we have $-4 + 7 = 3$; (H) Since $T_{-7} \circ T_{-4} = T_{-11}$ we have $-4 + -7 = -11$.

7. (A) the distance between consecutive points Xlml, Xml, Xl, X, Xm, Xlm, Xmlm will be the same as the distance between lines l and m.
(B) X = Xl, Xlml = Xml and Xlm = Xm. The distance from Xml to X and from X to Xm is twice the distance between lines l and m;
(C) If for example you choose Xm in Figure 16.5 to be X then you obtain the same points as in Figure 16.5 with different labels.

21.

8. (A) The distance between consecutive collinear points X_{OQO}, X_{QO}, X_O, X, X_Q, X_{OQ}, X_{QOQ} will be the distance from O to Q when X is chosen midway between O and Q. (B) The points X_{QO}, X, X_{OQ} will be collinear and the distance from one point to the next will be twice the distance from O to Q. The points X_{OQO}, X_O, X_Q, X_{QOQ} will also be collinear and the distance from one point to the next will also be twice the distance from O to Q; (C) All points determined will be collinear with O and Q. Points with an even number of subscripts in their names will be translation invariant as will points whose names have an odd number of subscripts. The distances will depend on the placement of X.

CHAPTER 17

Use the numbered figure to interpret answer for 1 and 2. Note that pieces 1 and 2 are congruent as are pieces 4 and 6.

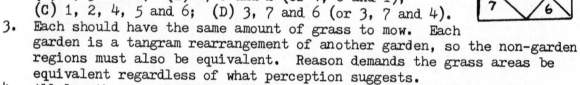

1. (A) 3 and 4 (or 3 and 6); (B) 1 and 2; (C) 1 and 7 (or 2 and 7); (D) 4 and 6; (E) 3 and 7.
2. (A) 4, 5 and 6; (B) 4, 6 and 2 (or 4, 6 and 1); (C) 1, 2, 4, 5 and 6; (D) 3, 7 and 6 (or 3, 7 and 4).
3. Each should have the same amount of grass to mow. Each garden is a tangram rearrangement of another garden, so the non-garden regions must also be equivalent. Reason demands the grass areas be equivalent regardless of what perception suggests.
4. All lengths are the same. Each is a tangram rearrangement of the others.
5. This is a direct comparison item. Note that angle A is a central angle and angle B is an inscribed angle. Both angles intercept the same arc. Hence the size of angle A should be twice that of angle B. This can be demonstrated empirically by cutting out two copies of B and putting them side by side to cover A.
6. C and D. Neither B nor E is a union of segments and so cannot be a tangram rearrangement of any segment.
7. (A) two pieces required; (B) three pieces required; (C) two pieces required; (D) five pieces required; (E) three pieces required; (F) four pieces required.
8. A (1 piece), B (2 pieces), C (2 pieces), D (2 pieces), E (2 pieces), F (2 pieces) are all tangram equivalent to A. G and H are not tangran equivalent to A.
9. Each demonstration can be made with two pieces. In fact each can be constructed using one duocube and the tricube which is a hexagonal prism.

CHAPTER 18

1. In each case the length of segment XY is the same as the length of segment WZ. The positions of the labels for the points and the presence or absence of objects between the points changes our perception of the distance.

2. (A) $|8-3| = 5$; (B) $|14- -5| = 19$; (C) $|-3.8- -2.4| = 1.4$;
    (D) $|0-3/8| = 3/8$; (E) $|\sqrt{2}- -3\sqrt{2}| = 4\sqrt{2}$; (F) $|\pi/2-5\pi/2| = \pi/8$;
    (G) $|\sqrt{8}-2\sqrt{2}| = 0$; (H) There is an errant point here. Should be
    $p = -135$, $q = 225$ so $|-135-225| = 360$.

3. Rulers A and B can be used directly assuming the end of the ruler
    is the zero point. Without this assumption PQ would be measured
    by using "2" as the left coordinate and subtracting it from the
    right coordinate. Rulers C, D and E have Q corresponding to
    "smudge" when P corresponds to 0. In these cases let P correspond
    to 1 and find length by subtracting 1 from coordinate of Q. Ruler F
    can be used directly, the smudge has no effect.

4. (A) $3+ 3\sqrt{2} +\sqrt{10}+\sqrt{13} \approx 13.9$; (B) $5 +\sqrt{10} +\sqrt{17} \approx 12.2$; (C) $4+4\sqrt{5}+4\sqrt{10}$
    ≈ 25.2; (D) $2+2\sqrt{10}+2\sqrt{13}+2\sqrt{17} \approx 23.6$; (E) $3+2\sqrt{2}+5\sqrt{5} \approx 16.8$;
    (F) $6+2\sqrt{2}+\sqrt{5}+3\sqrt{13} \approx 21.8$; (G) $6\sqrt{2}+4\sqrt{5} \approx 17.2$;
    (H) $3+2\sqrt{2}+2\sqrt{3}+2\sqrt{10}+\sqrt{13} \approx 20$.

5. (A) $\sqrt{2.08} \approx 1.4$; (B) $\sqrt{0.74} \approx 0.86$; (C) $\sqrt{70} \approx 8.37$; (D) $\sqrt{2.2161} \approx 1.49$;
    (E) $\sqrt{8} \approx 2.83$; (F) $\sqrt{36-(69/16)^2} \approx 4.17$.

6. (A) 6 to the nearest unit; (B) 3 to the nearest unit; (C) 4 to the
    nearest unit; (D) 5 to the nearest unit; (E) 7 to the nearest unit;
    (F) 2 to the nearest unit.

7. (A) 6 to the nearest half unit; (B) $3\frac{1}{2}$ to nearest half unit;
    (C) $4\frac{1}{2}$ to nearest half unit; (D) 5 to nearest half unit;
    (E) 7 to nearest half unit; (F) 2 to nearest half unit.

8. (A) 5 to nearest unit; A is tangram equivalent to a segment;
    (B) 5 to nearest unit; B is tangram equivalent to a segment;
    (C) approx 4 (no precision unit since not tangam equivalent to a
    segment. This is also true of D,E,F); (D) approx 5; (E) approx $5\frac{1}{2}$;
    (F) approx $5\frac{1}{2}$.

9. It can be appropriate to report a precision unit for A and B if
    each is rearranged to form a segment and then measured. Otherwise
    it is not appropriate. With C, D, E and F it is not appropriate
    because we approximate the curve by a union of segments and we don't
    know how good that approximation is.

10. They both have length 3π which can be deduced from the relation
    circumference is pi times diameter. This is not a question which can
    be answered by tangram rearrangement.

CHAPTER 19

1. In each case place vertex O at the center of the anglesizer so
    ray OM intersects point O. (A) 1/8; (B) $3\frac{1}{2}$; (C) $1\frac{1}{2}$; (D) $5\frac{1}{2}$;
    (Note we are measuring the amount of rotation in the direction
    indicated on the anglesizer. In A and C the clockwise direction is
    given, in B and D the counterclockwise direction is given.)

2. (A) 10; (B) 45; (C) 50; (D) 80; (E) 60; (F) 0; (G) 80; (H) 0.

3. (A) 60; (B) $127\frac{1}{2}$; (C) 210; (D) 540; (E) -90; (F) -270;
    (G) 780; (H) -990.

4. Answers are given considering the angle as directed. That is,the
    size of angle AQB is the amount of turn from QA to QB. If the
    angles are not considered as directed take the smallest of the
    absolute values of the answers given. eg for 90 or -30 take 30.

	AQB	BQC	AQC
(A)	100 (or -20)	90 (or -30)	70 (or -50)
(B)	300 (or -60)	270 (or -90)	210 (or -150)
(C)	450 (or -90)	330 (or -210)	240 (or -300)
(D)	10 (or -30)	15 (or -25)	25 (or -15)

5. These angles are all considered as undirected. Each estimate has precision unit of one anglesizer unit.
   (A) 1; (B) 2; (C) 5; (D) 3; (E) 7; (F) 11; (G) 6; (H) 2.

6. Each precision unit is half that used in exercise 5.
   (A) 1; (B) $2\frac{1}{2}$; (C) $4\frac{1}{2}$; (D) $3\frac{1}{2}$; (E) 7; (F) 11; (G) 6; (H) $1\frac{1}{2}$.

7. (A) 63; (B) 72; (C) 45; (D) 14; (E) 18; (F) 34; (G) 34; (H) 37;

8. (A) $90 + 18 = 108$; (B) $90 + 56 = 146$; (C) $27 + 27 = 54$; (D) $72 + 14 = 86$;
   (E) $56 - 18 = 38$; (F) $27 + 90 + 27 = 144$; (G) $27 - 14 = 13$;
   (H) $27 + 63 = 90$.

9. Draw a triangle using two corners A and B of the given page and the given point X as vertices. Locate the corresponding corners A' and B' on the second page. Use the anglesizer to measure angle ABX. Then draw a ray at B' so together with ray B'A' an angle of the same size as angle ABX is formed. Then use the anglesizer to measure angle BAX. Draw a ray at A' so together with ray A'B' an angle of the same size as angle BAX is formed. The two rays intersect at X' the point which corresponds to X.

CHAPTER 20

1. (A) 4; (B) 5; (C) 7; (D) 10; (E) 7; (F) 4; (G) 3; (H) 5;
   (I) $3\frac{1}{2}$; (J) $\frac{1}{4}$; (K) 2 2/3; (L) 3.

2. (A) partition into 5 right triangles with ares 1, 1, $\frac{1}{2}$, 2, 1 for total $5\frac{1}{2}$; (B) Partition into 4 right triangles with areas $1\frac{1}{2}$, 1, 1, $1\frac{1}{2}$ and one rectangle with area 2 for total 7; (C) Partition into four right triangles with areas 1, $\frac{1}{2}$, $1\frac{1}{2}$, 1 and two rectangles with areas 1 and 2 for total 7; (D) Partition into four right triangles each with area 1 and one rectangle with area 1 for total 5; (E) Partition into four right triangles with area 2, 1, 1, 1 and two rectangles each with area 2 for total 9; (F) Partition into eight right triangles, two with area 1 and six with area $\frac{1}{2}$ and one rectangle with area 2 for total 7; (G) Partition into four right triangles each with area $1\frac{1}{2}$ and one rectangle with area 4 for total 10; (H) Partition into four right triangles, two with area 1 and two with area $1\frac{1}{2}$ and one rectangle with area 2 for total 7.

3. (A) $16 - 4 - 4 - 2 = 6$; (B) $9 - 1\frac{1}{2} - 1\frac{1}{2} - 1\frac{1}{2} - \frac{1}{2} = 4$; (C) $9 - 1\frac{1}{2} - 1\frac{1}{2} - 2 = 4$;
   (D) $16 - 1\frac{1}{2} - 1 - 2 - 2 - 2 - 1\frac{1}{2} = 8$; (E) $15 - 1\frac{1}{2} - \frac{1}{2} - 1 - 1 - 1 - 1 - 1 = 8$;
   (F) $9 - 1\frac{1}{2} - 1 - 1\frac{1}{2} - \frac{1}{2} - \frac{1}{2} = 4$; (G) $12 - \frac{1}{2} - 1 - \frac{1}{2} - 1\frac{1}{2} - \frac{1}{2} - 1 = 7$; (H) $7 - \frac{1}{2} - \frac{1}{2} - \frac{1}{2} - \frac{1}{2} - \frac{1}{2} - \frac{1}{2} = 4$.

4. (A) $A = \frac{1}{2} \cdot 8 \cdot 3 = 12$; (B) $A = \frac{1}{2} \cdot 5 \cdot 3 = 7\frac{1}{2}$; (C) $A = 2 \cdot \frac{1}{2} \cdot 8 \cdot 2 = 16$;
   (D) $A = 2 \cdot \frac{1}{2} \cdot 10 \cdot 2 = 20$; (E) $A = 2 \cdot \frac{1}{2} \cdot 7 \cdot 3/2 = 10\frac{1}{2}$; (F) $A = 2 \cdot \frac{1}{2} \cdot 3 \cdot 4 + 4 \cdot 4 = 28$;
   (G) $A = \frac{1}{2} \cdot 4 \cdot 3 + 5 \cdot 2 = 16$; (H) $A = 2 \cdot \frac{1}{2} \cdot 4 \cdot 3 + 6 \cdot 3 = 30$; (I) $4 \cdot 3 + \frac{1}{2} \cdot 5 \cdot 3 = 19\frac{1}{2}$.

5. (A) (1, 13) so 7 to nearest 12; (B) (0, 9) so $4\frac{1}{2}$ to nearest 9;
   (C) (0, 10) so 5 to nearest 10; (D) (4, 16) so 10 to nearest 12;
   (E) (7, 23) so 15 to nearest 16; (F) (9, 23) so 16 to nearest 14;
   (G) (3, 20) so $11\frac{1}{2}$ to nearest 17; (H) (4, 22) so 13 to nearest 18;
   (I) (2, 24) so 13 to nearest 22.

6. (H) (32,66) so 49 to nearest 34 quarters, which is $12\frac{1}{4}$ to nearest $8\frac{1}{2}$ original units. This is more precise because $8\frac{1}{2}$ is less than 18, the precision unit obtained with the other grid. (I) (27, 72) so $49\frac{1}{2}$ to nearest 45 quarters, which is about 12 to nearest $11\frac{1}{4}$ original units. This is more precise because $11\frac{1}{4}$ is less then 22, the precision unit obtained with the larger grid. (Note that there is some judgement required in counting squares and that individual answers may differ slightly.)

7. Students should be advised to construct a circle and a grid to make the estimate. The figure in the text is too small for further refinement.

8. I is the inner measure and I + B is the outer measure. So the estimate is half the sum which is $\frac{1}{2}(I + (I + B)) = I + \frac{1}{2}B$. The precision unit is the difference which is $(I + B) - I = B$.

CHAPTER 21

1. (A) 44; (B) 50; (C) 48; (D) 46; (E) 48.

2. (A) $2 \cdot 3 \cdot 3 + 3 \cdot 2 \cdot 3 + 2 \cdot 3 \cdot 3 = 54$; (B) $2 \cdot 4 \cdot 4 + \frac{1}{2} \cdot 2 \cdot 2 \cdot 4 + \frac{1}{2} \cdot 1 \cdot 2 \cdot 4 = 44$;
   (C) $2 \cdot 5 \cdot 5 + \frac{1}{2} \cdot 1 \cdot 5 \cdot 5 = 62\frac{1}{2}$; (D) $\frac{1}{2} \cdot 2 \cdot 2 \cdot 6 + \frac{1}{2} \cdot 4 \cdot 2 \cdot 6 + \frac{1}{2} \cdot 3 \cdot 3 \cdot 6 + 4 \cdot 6 \cdot 6 = 207$;
   (E) $4 \cdot 3 \cdot 5 + 1 \cdot 5 \cdot 5 + 2 \cdot 3 \cdot 4 + \frac{1}{2} \cdot 2 \cdot 2 \cdot 4 = 117$; (F) $1 \cdot 6 \cdot 6 + 2 \cdot 3 \cdot 4 + 4 \cdot 3 \cdot 4 + \frac{1}{2} \cdot 3 \cdot 4 \cdot 4 = 132$;

3. (A) $2(24 + 9 + 18) = 102$; (B) $2(11 + 8) + 16 + 4 + 4(\sqrt{5} + \sqrt{8}) = 58 + 4(\sqrt{5} + \sqrt{8}) = 78$; (C) $2(25 + 10 + 15) + 5\sqrt{2} = 100 + 5\sqrt{2} \approx 107$;
   (D) $2 \cdot 34\frac{1}{2} + 9 \cdot 6 + 6 \cdot 6 + 3 \cdot 6 + 6(3\sqrt{2} + 2\sqrt{2} + 2\sqrt{5}) = 177 + 6(5\sqrt{2} + 2\sqrt{5}) \approx 246$;
   (E) $4 \cdot 25 + 2 \cdot 17 + 4 \cdot 2\sqrt{2} = 134 + 8\sqrt{2} \approx 145$; (F) $2(36 + 30) + 6 + 18 + 8 + 4 \cdot 5 = 184$.

4. (A) $3 \cdot 8 \cdot 3 - 1 \cdot 3 \cdot 3 - 1 \cdot 3 \cdot 3 = 54$; (B) $4 \cdot 4 \cdot 4 - \frac{1}{2} \cdot 2 \cdot 2 \cdot 4 - 1 \cdot 2 \cdot 4 - \frac{1}{2} \cdot 1 \cdot 2 \cdot 4 = 44$; (C) $3 \cdot 5 \cdot 5 - \frac{1}{2} \cdot 1 \cdot 5 \cdot 5 = 62\frac{1}{2}$; (D) $6 \cdot 9 \cdot 6 - \frac{1}{2}(2 \cdot 2 \cdot 6 + 2 \cdot 4 \cdot 6 + 3 \cdot 3 \cdot 6) - 3 \cdot 3 \cdot 6 = 207$; (E) $5 \cdot 5 \cdot 5 - \frac{1}{2} \cdot 2 \cdot 2 \cdot 4 = 117$; (F) $6 \cdot 6 \cdot 5 - \frac{1}{2} \cdot 4 \cdot 3 \cdot 4 - 2 \cdot 3 \cdot 4 = 132$.

5. (A) 0.54 units; (B) 0.44 units; (C) 0.625 units; (D) 2.07 units; (E) 1.17 units.

6. Prismlike figures are C, D, E, H, I, J. Volumes can be found by multiplying area of base by altitude assuming appropriate units are used.

7. (A) 1.0375 (not reasonable if compared with $(4/3)\pi r^3$ for $r = 0.5$)
   (B) 1.425 (probably an underestimate); (C) 1.3 (probably reasonable);
   (D) 13.2 (very close to estimate using inner and outer measure);
   (E) 30 (probably a close approximation); (F) 77.5 (probably an overestimate)

8. (A) this is prismlike so we can use special case of the cross section principle; also can use subtraction by comparing figure with elliptical "cylinder"; (B) subtraction seems most appropriate, compare with cube from which a pyramid is removed; (C) addition or subtraction seems most appropriate, compare with quarter cylinder; cross section principle might be used with vertical cross sections; (D) tangram rearrangement to a rectangular prism or addition strategy; (E) tangram rearrangement to a rectangular prism or addition or subtraction; (F) tangram rearrangement to a rectangular prism or addition or subtraction.

CHAPTER 14. Exercise 6.

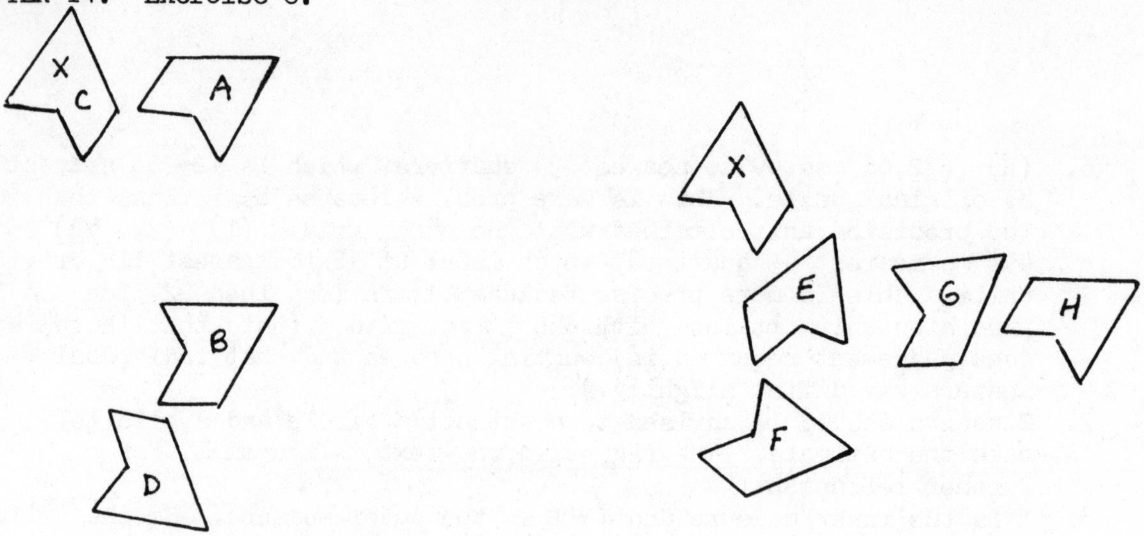

CHAPTER 22 Exercise 6.

(A)

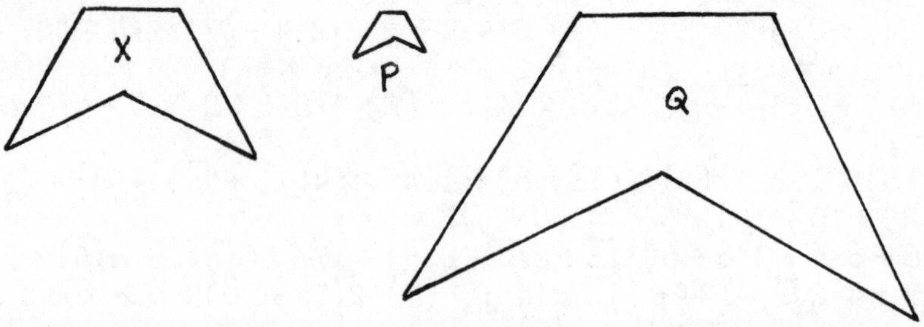

(B)

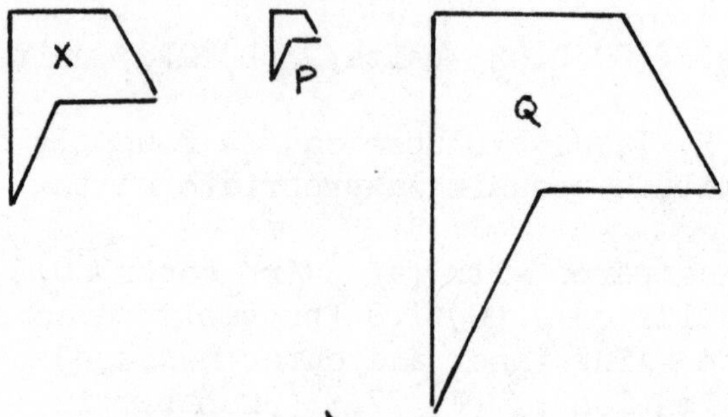

(C)

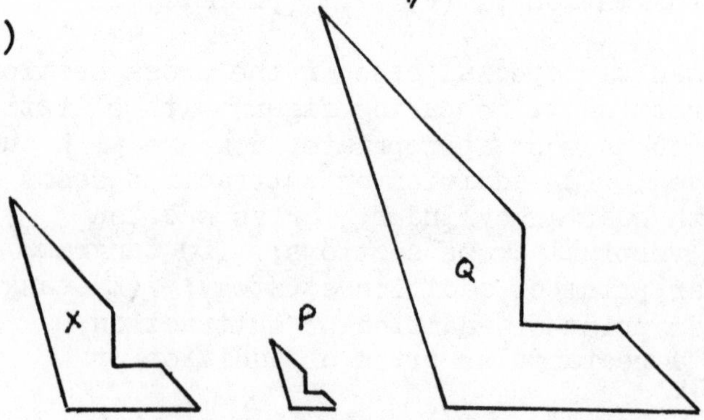

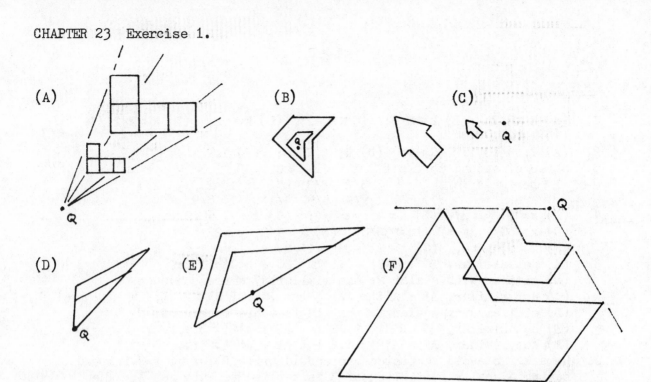

(A)

(B)

(C)

(D)

(E)

(F)

CHAPTER 22

1. (A) k = 3/2; (B) k = 2/3; (C) k = 2; (D) k = $\sqrt{2}$; (E) k = 2$\sqrt{2}$ /3;
    (F) k = 2.
2. (A) 1; (B) 1; (C) 4; (D) 4; (E) 8; (F) 1.
3. ratio of second to first   A   B   C   D   E   F
        perimeter   3/2   2/3   2/1 $\sqrt{2}$/1   2$\sqrt{2}$/3   2/1
        area   9/4   4/9   4/1   4/1   8/9   4/1
4. (A) x = 3, y = 8; (B) x = 4, y = 8/3; (C) x = 7, y = 9/4;
    (D) x = 60/7, y = 70/12 = 35/6; (E) x = 9/2, y = 27/8;
    (F) x = 8, y = 4, (G) x = 21/4, y = 15/2.
5. (A) not similar, BC : B'C' = 1:1 but DC : D'C' = 1:2;
    (B) similar with scalar 2, one similarity correspondence;
    (C) not similar, AB : A'B' = $\sqrt{2}$: 5 but BC : B'C' = 2:$\sqrt{5}$;
    (D) similar with scalar 1, that is they are congruent;
    (E) not similar, BC : B'C' = 1:$\sqrt{2}$ but AB : A'B' = 3 : 2$\sqrt{2}$;
    (F) not similar, AF : A'F' = 1:2 but AB : A'B' = 3:4.
6. Remark: To avoid confusion one should write P : X = 1 : 3 instead of
    saying a scalar multiplier of 3 is applied to P to get X. Then
    we would have Q : X = 2 : 1 instead of applying a factor of $\frac{1}{2}$ to Q
    to obtain X. From P : X = 1 : 3 and Q : X = 2 : 1 we obtain X : Q = 3:6
    and finally P : Q = 1 : 6. Hence Q could be obtained from P by
    applying a scaling factor of 6. Examples are given on sketch page 26.
7. (A) 4/3 m; (B) 8/9 sq m; (C) 64/27 (approx 2.4 times); (D) congruent,
    same anglesize; (E) V'R'P' is 4/3 as long as VRP; (F) 16/9;
    (G) approx 52.7 cu in; (H) 37$\frac{1}{2}$ cm.

CHAPTER 23

1. See sketch page 27.
2. (A) The figures are not quite similar but construction error may
    result in conclusion they are similar with scalar apprimately 2;
    (B) The triangles are centrally similar with scalar approximately 2;
    (C) The figures are not centrally similar; (D) The figures have
    opposite orientation and cannot be centrally similar; (E) The figures
    are not quite centrally similar but construction error might result
    in conclusion they are similar with scalar approximately 4/3;
    (F) The rays are not parallel so they cannot be centrally similar;
    (G) All parallel but not congruent segments are centrally similar;
    (H) The triangles are congruent so they cannot be centrally similar;
    there is a turn center for a congruence but not a center for a
    central similarity; (I) The figures are centrally similar with
    scalar approximately 3.
3. (A) This requires a rotation to get corresponding sides parallel.
    The test should reveal they are similar heptiamonds; (B) This requires
    a rotation of $\frac{1}{4}$ turn to get corresponding sides parallel. The test
    should reveal they are similar; (C) This requires a rotation to
    get corresponding sides parallel. The test should reveal they are
    not similar; (D) This requires a reflection to get orientation the
    same and corresponding sides parallel. The test is fairly close
    but reveals the figures are not similar.

4. All squares are similar. Each square has a center of symmetry where the diagonals intersect. Given any two squares they can be positioned so their centers of symmetry coincide and their sides are respectively parallel. Then the common center of symmetry is also a center for a central similarity.

5. B, C, D and E are pyramidlike. In fact E is a pyramid.

6. (A) 128 sq cm; (B) $12\frac{1}{2}$ sq cm; (C) 800/3 cu cm; (D) ratio is 5:8; (E) less than half since 25/64 is less than $\frac{1}{2}$; (F) approx 254 cu in; (G) approx 238 cu in; (H) $125/512 \approx 0.24$.

7. (A) approx 16.8; (B) 36; (C) approx 104; (D) approx 556;

8. Answers should be self checking with the knowledge that $4 \cdot \frac{1}{2} = 2$, $1/2 \cdot 1/3 = 1/6$; $3 \cdot 4 = 12$; $2/3 \cdot 3/4 = 1/2$.

CHAPTER 24

1. (A) $(7\frac{1}{2}, 8\frac{1}{2})$ and $8 \pm \frac{1}{2}$; (B) (4.05, 4.15) and 4.1 ± 0.05; (C) (10, 14) and 12 ± 2; (D) $(17\frac{1}{2}, 22\frac{1}{2})$ and $20 \pm 2\frac{1}{2}$; (E) (13 3/4, 14 1/4) and $14 \pm \frac{1}{4}$; (F) (4 7/16, 4 9/16) and $4\frac{1}{2} \pm 1/16$; (G) $(34\frac{1}{2}, 37\frac{1}{2})$ and $36 \pm 1\frac{1}{2}$; (H) (0.68, 0.72) and 0.7 ± 0.02.

2. (A) 10 cm to nearest 4 cm; (B) $3\frac{1}{2}$ in to nearest $\frac{1}{2}$ in; (C) 9 in to nearest 2 in; (D) 0.025 to nearest 0.01; (E) 6 ft to nearest $\frac{1}{2}$ ft; (F) 94 sq cm to nearest 8 sq cm; (G) 8.1 cm to nearest 0.2 cm; (H) 4 5/8 yd to nearest $\frac{1}{2}$ yd.

3.

	most precise	most accurate
(A)	same precision	16 cu cm to nearest cu cm
(B)	40 m to nearest 2 m	40 m to nearest 2 m
(C)	10 sq in to 1/10 sq in	same accuracy
(D)	36 cm to nearest 4 cm	same accuracy
(E)	(12, 16)	(12, 16)
(F)	(12, 16)	same accuracy
(G)	(13, 15)	(13, 15)
(H)	same precision	(13, 17)
(I)	same precision	20 ± 2
(J)	20 ± 0.2	20 ± 0.2
(K)	7 ft ± 0.5 ft	same accuracy
(L)	60 min ± 0.3 min	90 min ± 0.4 min

4. Precision unit for length is the distance between consecutive marks on the ruler. Precision unit for anglesizer is the size of an angle formed by two consecutive marks on the "outside" of the anglesizer and the center of the anglesizer. In comparison with the reporting units the precision units are as follows: (A) 1/3; (B) 10; (C) $\frac{1}{2}$; (D) 1/8; (E) 30; (F) 1/6; (G) $\frac{1}{2}$; (H) $\frac{1}{4}$.

5. (A) 14 squares; (B) 10 squares; (C) 12 squares; (D) 14 squares.

6. (A) 7/2; (B) 24; (C) 15; (D) 36; (E) 27/4; (F) 1.07

7. (A) 16 1/12; (B) 128 2/3; (C) 58 2/3; (D) 43333 1/3; (E) 20833 1/3; (F) 10141 2/3.

8. (1A) 15/16; (1B) $4.05/4.1 \approx 0.988$; (1C) 5/6; (1D) 7/8; (2E) 23/24; (2F) $90/94 \approx 0.96$; (2G) $80/81 \approx 0.99$; (2H) $35/37 \approx 0.95$

9.

accuracy	lengths of bases	heights	areas
(6A)	7/8	5/6	$57/64 \approx 0.89$
(6B)	3/4	7/8	$476/512 \approx 0.93$
(6C)	18/19	10/11	$3881/3971 \approx 0.98$
(6D)	8/9	8/9	$954/972 \approx 0.98$

1.	2. Impossible. A curve has two or no endpoints.	3.	4.	5.
6. Impossible. Number of tracings always even. (Reversals)	7.	8. is equiv to	9. are not equivalent but $R = 3$.	10. are equivalent

CHAPTER 2 CONSTRUCTIONS

1.	2. Impossible Every curve has at least two non-separating points.	3.	4.	5.
6.	7. Impossible. Regions are not subsets of curves so they cannot separate.	8. Shaded region separates into 2 comp.	9. Impossible. No cross section of a sphere is a square.	10. Impossible.

1.	2.	3.	4.	5.
	V = 4 A = 4	V = 4 A = 5		
6. Impossible Each arc has two endpoints.	7.	8.	9.	10.

CHAPTER 4 CONSTRUCTIONS

1.	2.	3.	4.	5.
Segment AB separates line.	2. Impossible. By definition a segment is bounded.	3. ray or half-line	4.	5.
6. Impossible A segment is dense.	7.	8. Impossible. Intersection is ray or point or empty set.	9. Graph is a line.	10. Impossible 1 or 3 pts possible but not 2.

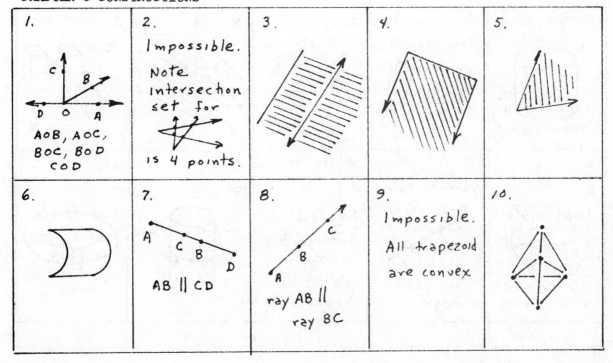

1.

2.

3.

4.
Impossible. Pentagon has at least two diagonals.

5.
6 sides 9 diagonals

6.
Impossible. Vertices on circle imply convex.

7.

8.

9.

10.
Impossible. Hexagons have six vertices.

CHAPTER 6 CONSTRUCTIONS

1.
AOB, AOC, BOC, BOD COD

2.
Impossible. Note intersection set for
is 4 points.

3.

4.

5.

6.

7.
AB ∥ CD

8.
ray AB ∥ ray BC

9.
Impossible. All trapezoid are convex

10.

CHAPTER 7 CONSTRUCTIONS

1.	2.	3.	4.	5. Impossible. All vertices of prism are of order 3.
6.	7.	8.	9.	10.

CHAPTER 8 CONSTRUCTIONS

1.	2.	3.	4.	5.
6. six pyramids pack cube	7. Impossible One base edge is skew to at least 1 non base edge.	8. P, q, R, S not coplanar	9. line	10. "line"

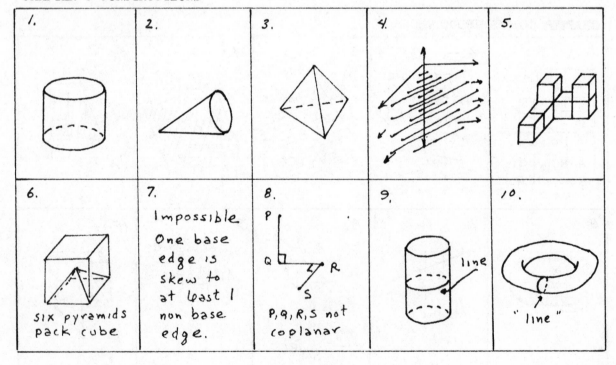

CHAPTER 9 CONSTRUCTIONS

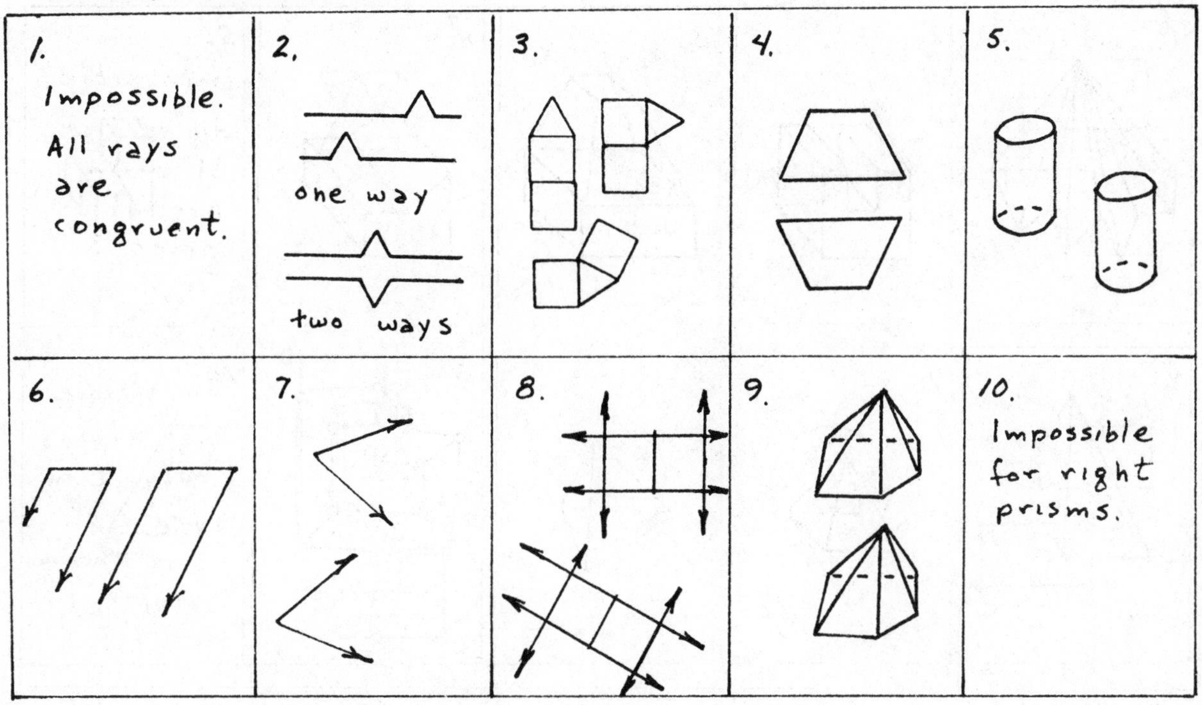

1. Impossible. All rays are congruent.	**2.** one way / two ways	**3.**	**4.**	**5.**
6.	**7.**	**8.**	**9.**	**10.** Impossible for right prisms.

CHAPTER 10 CONSTRUCTIONS

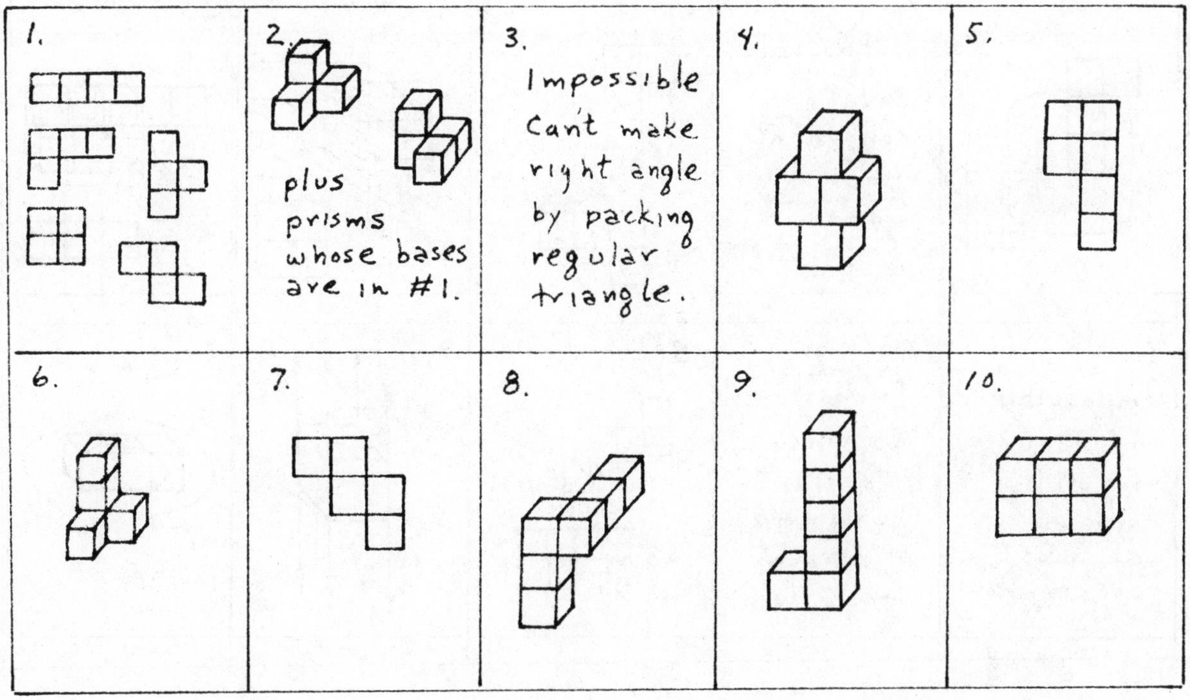

1.	**2.** plus prisms whose bases are in #1.	**3.** Impossible can't make right angle by packing regular triangle.	**4.**	**5.**
6.	**7.**	**8.**	**9.**	**10.**

CHAPTER 11 CONSTRUCTIONS

1.

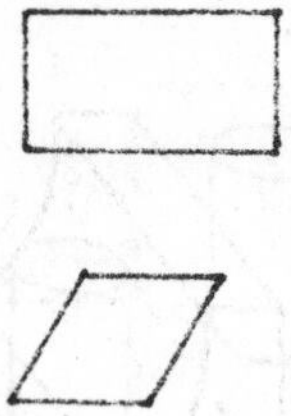

2.

3. Impossible. Perpendicular bisector of segment determined by centers is refl line.

4.

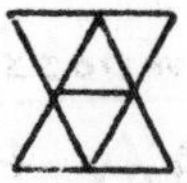

5.

6.

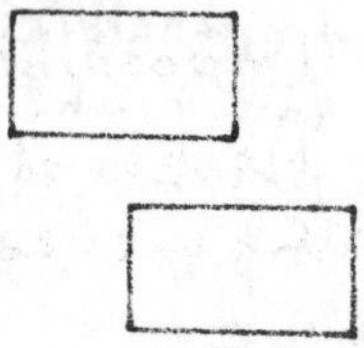

7.

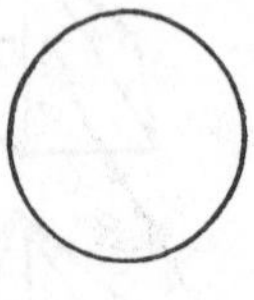

8.

9. A' D' B' C' A B C D

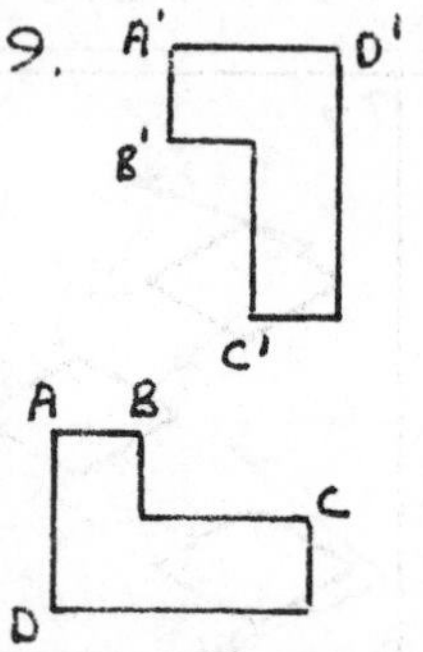

10 Impossible Can always reflect in vertical line through center.

CHAPTER 12 CONSTRUCTIONS

1.

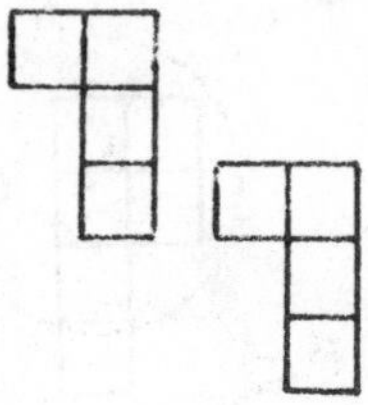

2. Impossible. Rotation congruent implies same orientation.

3.

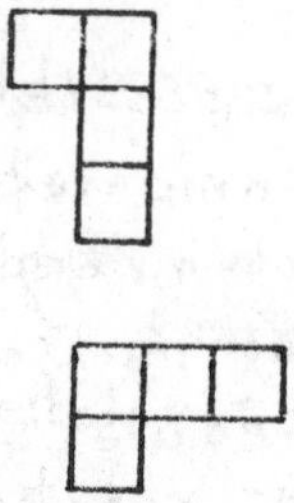

4.

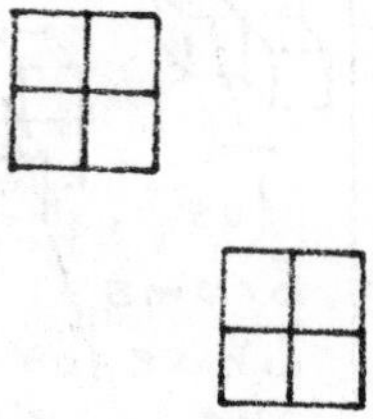

5.

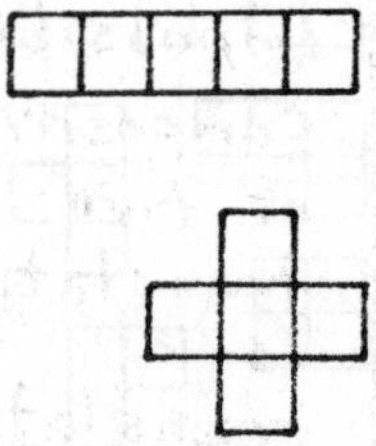

6. Impossible Bounded figures can have at most one center.

7. Impossible. Rotation invariant hexomino invariant for ½ turn

8.

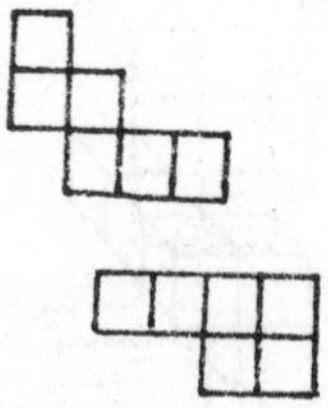

9.

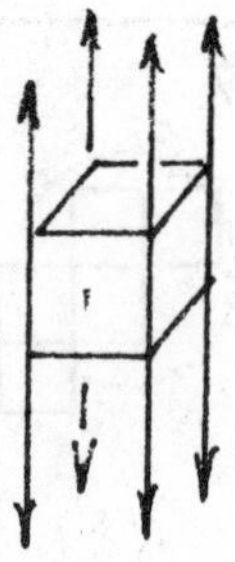

10.

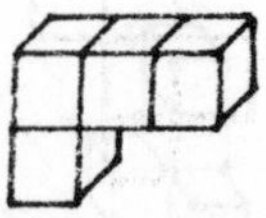

CHAPTER 13 CONSTRUCTIONS

1.	2.	3.	4.	5.
	Impossible. Any two congruent circles are translation congruent.			

6.	7.	8.	9.	10.
		Impossible. There can be at most one translation correspondence.	 AB & BC	Impossible. No bounded figure can be translation invariant.

CHAPTER 14 CONSTRUCTIONS

1.	2.	3.	4.	5.
Impossible. Composition of two translations is a translation		Impossible. Composition of reflections is translation or rotation		

6.	7.	8.	9.	10.

1.
 	
invariance is trivial rotation
	2.
	
	two rot
	
	one rot one refl.
		3.
		
		19
			4.
			
			F • A •
			  • B
			E • o
			  • C
			  • D
			
			$R_{600°} R_{AOF}$
				5.
				
				R_5, R_4, R_3
				R_2, R_1, R_0
				must be invariances.

6. Impossible. If there is at least 1 reflection there must be an even number	7. ○	8.	9. Eight reflection invariances implies 8 rotation invariances (16 in all).	10. 12 invariances

1.	2. Impossible. Translation invariant for 1 cm implies tran invariant for 2, 3, 4, ...	3. Any figure invariant for T_{AB} is also invariant for T_{BA}. $AB \neq BA$.	4. Must be invariant for vectors which are multiples of 0.25 cm.	5. Impossible to have just two parallel lines of symmetry. It's one or infinitely many.
6. Impossible. Translation invariant & one line of symmetry implies infinitely many.	7. Impossible. Translation invariant & one turn center implies infinitely many.	8. Impossible. Two turn centers implies infinitely many.	9. Any point of figure 16.1 can be used as origin.	10. H or D ? ? +1 0 +1

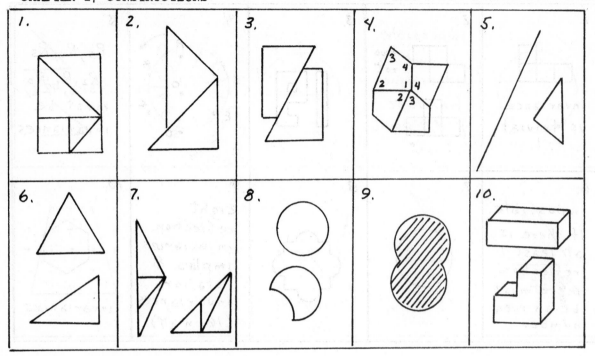

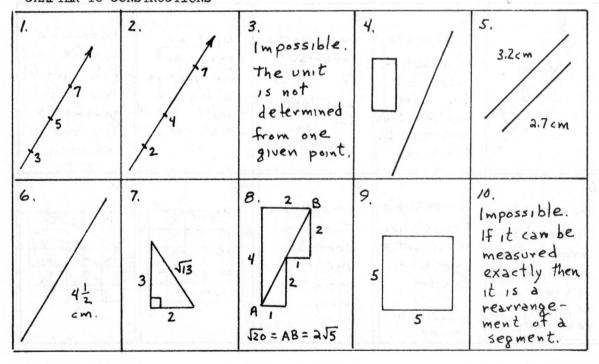

CHAPTER 19 CONSTRUCTIONS

1.	2.	3.	4.	5.
(circle with marks 4, 2, 7)	Impossible. No unit is determined from one given point	(semicircle with marks 4 3 2, 5 6 1)	(clock-like circle with marks 2 1, 3 0, 4 6, 5)	$(37\frac{1}{2}, 42\frac{1}{2})$

6.	7.	8.	9.	10.
(angle) eg 58°	(angle) eg 56°	(geoboard V shape) 14 + 34 = 48	(geoboard rhombus)	(geoboard trapezoid)

CHAPTER 20 CONSTRUCTIONS

1.	2.	3.	4.	5.
(pentagon/house shape) it packs!	(square with inner square) 1cm / 1in.	(geoboard quadrilateral)	(geoboard L-shape)	(geoboard arrow shape)

6.	7.	8.	9.	10.
Impossible. All geoboard polygons have areas which can be determined exactly.	(two triangles)	(triangle and rectangle)	(grid square with F, A, E, D, B, C)	(grid square with triangles)

CHAPTER 21 CONSTRUCTIONS

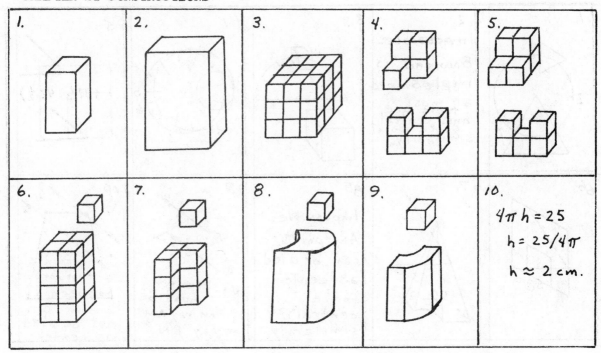

CHAPTER 22 CONSTRUCTIONS

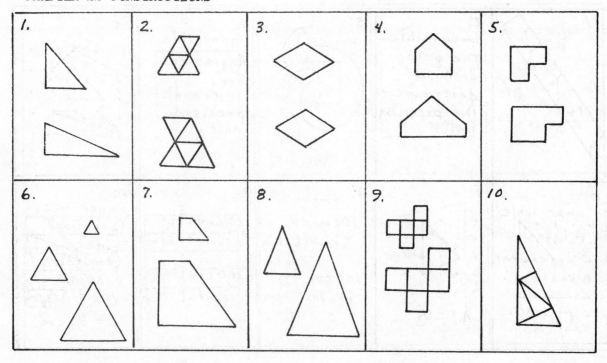

1. 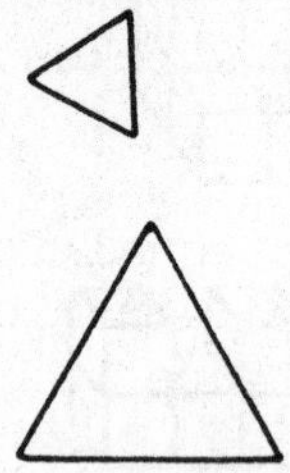	2. Impossible. Bounded implies at most one central similarity.	3. 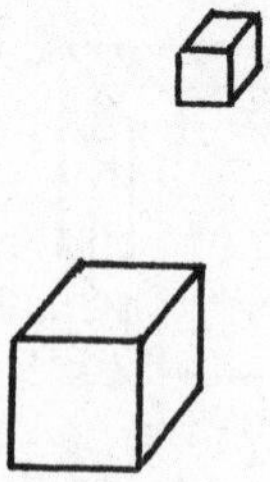	4. 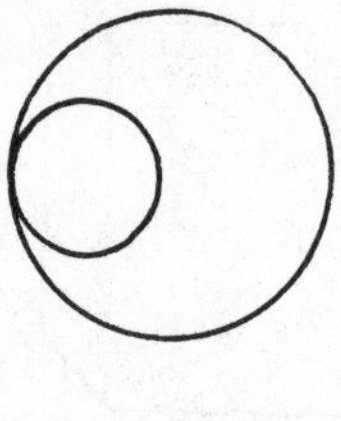	5. 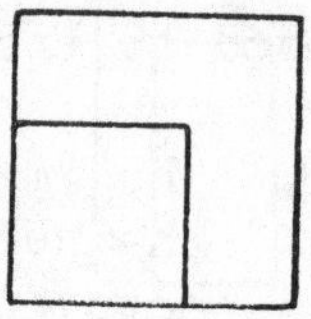
6. 	7. 	8. Impossible. Any point can be used as center for a central similarity.	9. 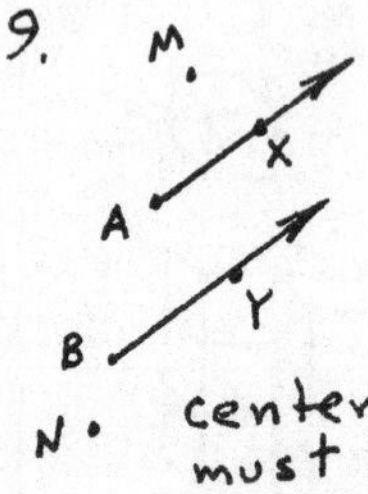 M· A X B Y N· center must be on ray AM or ray BN.	10. 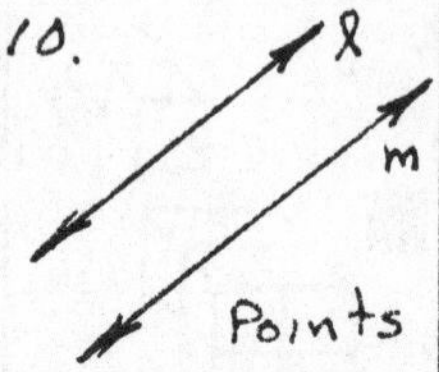 ℓ m Points on or between ℓ and m can not be used as centers.

CHAPTER 24 CONSTRUCTIONS

1. 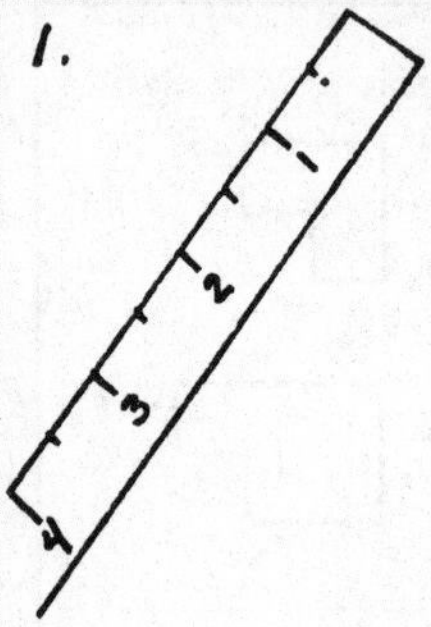	2. Impossible. The grid does not determine the precision unit.	3. 	4. Impossible. Anglesizer does determine precision unit.	5. 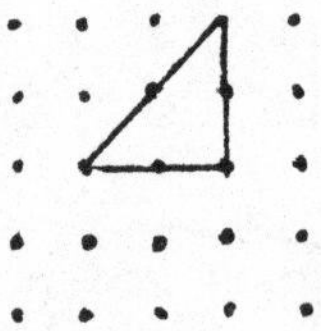
6. 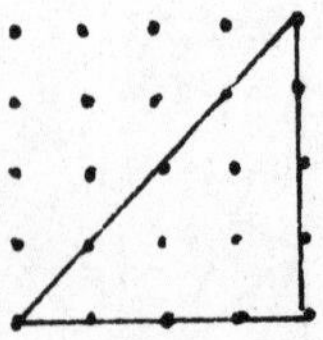 A.I = 3/4	7. 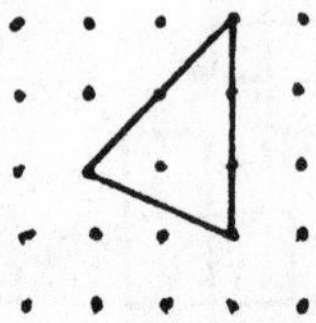 A.I = 1/3	8. 10cm to nearest 1cm 100cm to nearest 1cm.	9. 10cm to nearest 1cm. 100cm to nearest 10cm	10. inner meas (2-p)(3-p) outer meas (2+p)(3+p) precision 10p = 1 sq cm p = 1/10 cm.

1 A.   The first figure is a curve. It can be traced by starting at any
       point and finishing at the same point. The remaining figures can
       be traced in four, three, six, two and five strokes, respectively.
This problem provides an opportunity to explore the relationship between
the number of odd vertices (defined on pg 29) and the number of strokes
needed to trace.

1 B.   The immediate conjecture is that the number of regions is equal to
       the number of crossing points. The number must be counted dynamically
       however. If a point is crossed twice (like the second figure in
Figure 1.23) then it must be counted twice. Each crossing creates one
region. If you end at a point which is already a point of the curve that
must be counted as a crossing point.

1 C.   This problem provides good practice in recognizing topologically
       equivalent curves. Pictured below are three region curves that are
       not equivalent. One way to generate examples is to draw those with
one crossing point, then those with two and finally those with three crossing points. There is only one closed curve which encloses one region; it
is simple. For two regions, there is only one closed curve, a figure eight.
For three regions the three loop petal and the three loop chain (defined
in problem E) are the only nonequivalent curves.

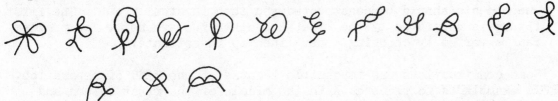

1 D.   Every nonsimple curve can be traced in some number of ways which is
       a multiple of four. There is a choice of ends in an open curve and
       a choice of direction in a loop. Curves with N linked loops can be
traced in 2^{n+1} ways. Examples of some curves that can be traced in a
number of ways not a power of two are given.

| 8 | 12 | 24 | 48 | 360 |

1 E.   This problem helps to distinguish between orientation and number of
       tracings. N-loops and N-chains can all be traced in infinitely
       many ways since any point can be used as a start point. Once a start
point is chosen there are a finite number of tracings. Each N-loop or
N-chain can be oriented in 2^N ways since each loop can be oriented in
two ways independent of the other loops.

1 F.   For the first figure, points on the loop have circuit number 1,
       points not on the loop have circuit number 0. For the figure eight,
       the crossing point has circuit number 2, the other points have circuit
number 1. In the third figure the two crossing points have circuit number 2,

the other points have circuit number 1. The fourth figure has every point
with circuit number 4 except the crossing points which have circuit number
6. It is very time consuming to find circuit numbers for all points on
the last curve. Students might be asked to find circuit numbers for three
different points. One systemmatic way of counting circuits is to label
the crossing points and to make a tree diagram with root at the starting
point of the circuit. This technique reveals that a point on the bottom
of the curve has circuit number 10, one on the side has circuit number 11
and one on top has circuit number 8.
All points of a simple open curve have circuit number 0. All points of a
simple closed curve have circuit number 1. All points on the loops of an
N-loop petal have circuit number 1, the center point has circuit number N.
All points on the loops of an N-loop chain have circuit number 1, all crossing points have circuit number 2.

2 A. An N-loop chain has exactly N-1 separating points. No curve consists
  ■   entirely of separating points. A simple open curve has two non-
       separating points. To be a nonseparating point is to be an endpoint
or a point on a loop. If a loop exists on a curve the curve must have
infinitely many non separating points. If there are endpoints and no
loops there must be two endpoints.

2 B. The objects should be constructed and then physically cut. The first
  ■   figure is separated by the line; the other two are not. The problem
       can be varied by choosing other lines to investigate.

2 C. Some constructions are impossible because of one kind of separation.
  ■   An example is to place an X in the middle of the first column and
       another in the middle of the fifth column. Then place a Y in the
middle of the first row and another in the middle of the fifth row. Any
path connecting the Xs will separate the Ys and any path that connects the
Ys will separate the Xs. Another kind of separation occurs when a path
connecting two points does not leave enough remaining points to construct
a path to connect other points. Students should find examples of both
kinds of separation.

2 D. Every point except the endpoints of a simple open curve is a separat-
  ■   ing point. Every arc that is a subset of a simple open curve but
       does not contain an endpoint of the curve is a separating arc. A
simple closed curve has no separating points and no separating arcs. A
non simple curve need not have separating points. A quadrilateral with a
diagonal is an example. However they must have non separating points. The
diagonal of a polygon is a separating arc for the curve which consists of
the polygon together with the diagonal. Non simple curves must have infinitely
many separating arcs.

2 E. Two simple closed curves may create any number of regions greater
  ■   than two. If the two curves are circles or squares then either three
       or four regions are created depending on whether the interiors do
not or do intersect. Three circles may determine four, five, six ,seven

44.

or eight regions. Four regions are formed if no two circles intersect.
The remaining cases are constructed by beginning with two circles forming
four regions. A third circle can be added so that it intersects one, two,
three or four of these regions creating a total of five, six, seven or
eight regions. Four circles may determine any number of regions from
five through fourteen. Constructions for five, six, seven, eight or nine
intersections can be made by adding a circle which does not intersect any
of the circles in the three circle case. Constructions for ten, eleven,
twelve, thirteen and fourteen regions begins with the three circles forming eight regions. A fourth circle is added so that it intersects two,
three, four, five or six of those regions. The strategy for squares follows
that for circles.

2 F. The maze does not separate the plane. There are two paths from X
to Y in the maze. If there were no path from X to Y then the maze
would have to separate the plane. There is one path from M to N in
the maze. A good maze should not separate the plane but the fact that it
does not should not be evident to a casual observer.

3 A. The idea of this problem is to get students to generate networks and
to make comparisons. They need not find all of the networks to benefit
from the search for them. Some may be persuaded to go on to networks
with five arcs. The networks with three and four arcs are drawn below.

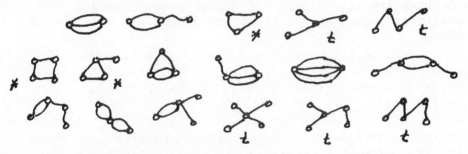

3 B. The generalization to be discovered is that a network having A arcs,
V vertices and R regions will have $V + R = A + 2$. Note that this counts
the exterior as a region.

3 C. If a network is traceable there will be either no odd vertices or
two odd vertices. If there are no odd vertices the tracing is a closed
curve. If N strokes are required to trace a curve there are 2N
odd vertices.

3 D. The following combinations are possible.

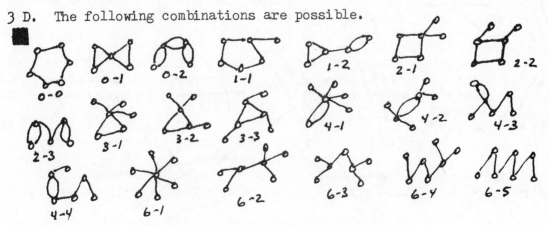

3 E. The networks having no multiple arcs and having a total of three or
      four arcs are marked in the answer to problem A. Those with an asterisk
      or a t do not have multiple arcs. Those with a t are trees. There
      are six networks with five arcs having no multiple arcs and are not
trees. They appear below. The five arc trees are given in the last line.

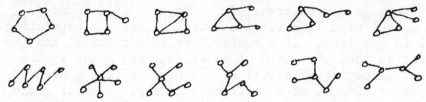

3 F. The first two maps can be colored with two colors. The other three
      can be colored with three colors but not with two. Two colors will
      always be sufficient for line maps and for circle maps. No map
requires more than four colors.

4 A. Four points determine 1, 4 or 6 lines depending on whether all four
      points are collinear, three points are collinear or no three points
      are collinear. Five points determine 1, 5, 6, 8 or 10 lines. One
line is determined if all five points are collinear. Five lines are
determined if exactly four points are collinear. Ten lines are determined
if no three points are collinear. The other cases are shown below. Six
points determine 1, 6, 8, 9, 10, 11, 13 or 15 lines. The more obvious
generalizations are: if n points are arranged with exactly n-1 of them
collinear then n lines are determined; if n points are arranged with no
three of them collinear then n(n-1)/2 lines are determined and this is
the maximum number.

For those who continue on to seven or eight points students have found
these numbers of lines determined by seven points; 1, 7, 10, 11, 12, 14 ,
16, 17, 19, 21 and these numbers for eight points: 1, 8, 13, 14, 16, 17,
18, 19, 20, 23, 24, 26, 28.

4 B. With four lines there may be 0, 1, 3, 4, 5 or 6 points of intersection.
      With five lines there may be 0, 1, 4, 5, 6, 7, 8, 9 or 10 points of
      intersection.

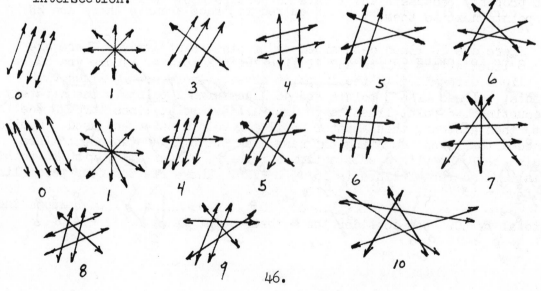

4 C.   1 is not true. As a counterexample, a segment is a bounded
■   connected subset of a line but its endpoints are not separating
       points. 2 is not true. If a number line is horizontal and the
integer a is negative then the graph of $ax \leq b$ is a ray going to the
right. 3 is true. A connected subset of a line is either a segment
(open or half-open or closed) or a halfline or a ray. Each of these has
infinitely many separating points. 4 is not true. Figure 4.13 is a
counterexample. 5 is true. A separating set for a line must have points
on either side of it. That makes it bounded. 6 is true. Every finite
set of points which is collinear has two points which are further apart
than any other pair of points. The segment having those endpoints will
contain all of the other points.

4 D.   Not all of the points X, Y, Z must exist. If all three exist they
■   are collinear. If none of the points exist then there are three
       parallel lines. If two points, say X and Y, exist then line XY
is parallel to segments A_2B_3 and A_3B_2. Similar possibilities exist when
the points are located on a circle. For some locations of the As and Bs
on a square we expect the same result as before. For instance if all As
are collinear and all Bs are collinear we are back to the first case.
Similarly if all As and Bs are points where a circle intersects the square
then we are back to the second case. In general there is no pattern for
the points X, Y and Z determined by As and Bs on a square.

4 E.   The set in Figure 4.17 is not dense. There is no point between
■ A_n and A_{n+1} for any n nor any point between B_n and B_{n+1} for any n.
       There are infinitely many points between C and A_n for any n and
between C and B_m for any m and between A_n and B_m for any m,n. The set
does not have the next point property because C has no point next to it.
All other points have points next to them. The set in Figure 4.18 is
not dense. There is no point between B_n and B_{n+1} or between A_n and A_{n+1}
for any m,n. There are infinitely many points between A and any other
point or between B and any other point. The set does not have the next
point property because A and B have no next points. All other points
have points next to them.

4 F.   There are 20 lines determined by a nine point array. There are
■   8 lines with 3 points and 12 lines with 2 points. There are 62
       lines determined by the 16 point array. There are 10 lines with
4 points, 4 lines with 3 points and 48 lines with 2 points. One strategy
for counting two point lines is to draw all two point lines through one
point, then another, then another until all points have been used. Caution
is needed to prevent counting the same line twice. The two point lines
can also be found with a subtraction strategy. For example, with 16 points
the maximum number of lines is $16 \cdot 15/2 = 120$. There are ten four point lines.
Each four point line could determine $4 \cdot 3/2 = 6$ lines if the points were not
collinear. So we count 1 instead of 6 on ten occasions. That reduces the
120 total by 50. Now consider the 4 three point lines.

5 A. To get a maximum number of collinear vertices you need to get off
a base line and then back on as often as you can with the number of
edges available. The pattern can be described as a sequence by
many students. For polygons with 3, 4, 5, 6, ... sides the maximum number
of collinear vertices is 2, 2, 3, 4, 4, 5, 6, 6, 7, 8, 8, 9, 10, 10, ...
An algebraic description of the relation follows. If n is the number of
sides of a polygon and m is the maximum number of collinear vertices then

when $n \equiv 0 \pmod 3$ $m = (2/3) n$
when $n \equiv 1 \pmod 3$ $m = (2/3)(n-1)$
when $n \equiv 2 \pmod 3$ $m = (2/3)(n-2) + 1$.

Some pictures which suggest how to construct examples follow.

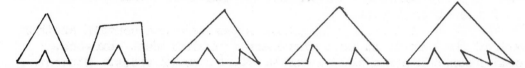

5 B. The minimum number of diagonals in a hexagon is three; the maximum
is nine. All numbers between three and nine are possible. The
minimum number of diagonals in an n-sided polygon is n-3; the
maximum is n(n-3)/2. All numbers in between are possible. The maximum
is attained when the polygon is convex. In that case each vertex is an
endpoint for n-3 diagonals. Concave polygons have less than the maximum
number of diagonals. The minimum is achieved by placing n-3 points in the
interior of a triangle. A figure for n = 7 is illustrated below.

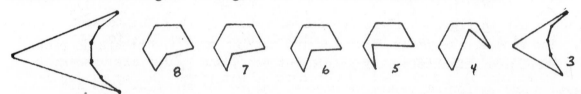

5 C. All triangles have the packing property. All quadrilaterals have
the packing property. The packing of a general quadrilateral depends
on the fact that the sum of the degree measures of the four angles
is 360. Four copies of a quadrilateral can be packed around a point. (This
fact has not been developed in the text but is known to most students).
A discovery within the reach of many students is that any pentagon that
has two parallel sides will pack the plane. An example of a packing for
a general quadrilateral and a pentagon with two parallel sides is given.

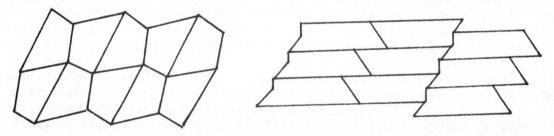

5 D. There is one given triangulation in which all three diagonals have
an endpoint at B. There are five others in which all three diagonals
have an endpoint at A, C, D, E or F. There is another triangulation
given in which three vertices B, D and F are endpoints of diagonals.

There is another triangulation using A, C and E. Not given is an example
of a triangulation in which two vertices are endpoints of two diagonals
and two other vertices are endpoints of one diagonal. An example of this
is AC, CF and FD. There are five other triangulations of this type.
There are 42 ways to divide a heptagon into triangles. There are seven
ways for each of six types. The types are illustrated below.

 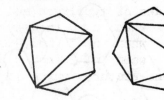

5 E.   There are three different pentagons. A pentagon can contain another
       polygon of 8, 9 or 10 sides. There are four different hexagons.
       A hexagon can contain a polygon of 9, 10, 11 or 12 sides. Students
may recognize that a convex polygon with n sides can contain a polygon
with 2n sides. Each reflex angle reduces the number of sides in the
contained polygon by 1. The number of reflex angles in an n-gon is at
most n-3. So an n-gon can contain a polygon having between n+3 and
2n sides. Figures for different pentagons and hexagons appear below.

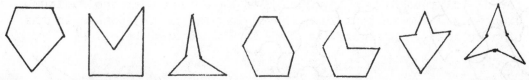

5 F.   The middle hexagon in Figure 5.20 does not pack; the others do pack.
       So not all equiangular hexagons pack the plane. The first hexagon
       in Figure 5.21 does pack; the others do not pack. So not all equi-
lateral hexagons pack the plane.

6 A.   The table looks like the one below:

lines	1	2	3	4	5	6	7	8	9	10
intersections	0	1	3	6	10	15	21	28	36	45
separated sets	2	4	7	11	16	22	29	37	46	56

If n is the number of lines than the number of intersections is n(n-1)/2.
The number of separated sets is $\frac{1}{2}n^2 + \frac{1}{2}n + 1$. Most students will have trouble
finding explicit formulas but will be able to describe patterns recursively.
They may say the number of intersections starts at zero and the differences
follow the sequence 1, 2, 3, 4 ... They may say that the number of separated
sets starts at 2 and the differences follow the sequence 2, 3, 4, 5 ...

6 B.   If the five points are coplanar then only one plane is determined.
       If A, B, C and D are coplanar and P is not in the plane determined
       by A, B, C and D then seven planes are determined. The seven planes
are ABP, ACP, ADP, BCP, BDP, CDP, ABCD. A third case has A, B, C and D
coplanar with A, B and C collinear and P not in plane ABCD. In this case
five planes are determined. The planes are ABCD, ABCP, ADP, CDP and BDP.
The fourth case is when no four of the five points are coplanar. Then
each set of three points determines a unique plane. If the points are

K, L, M, N and O then the ten planes are KLM, KLN, KLO, KMN, KMO, KNO, LMN, LMO, LNO and MNO. There is one more case and it is trivial. If all five points are collinear then no plane is determined.

6 C. All of the figures pack except for the fifth and sixth figures. The second packing requires that some of the copies be flipped over. Hints for packing patterns follow.

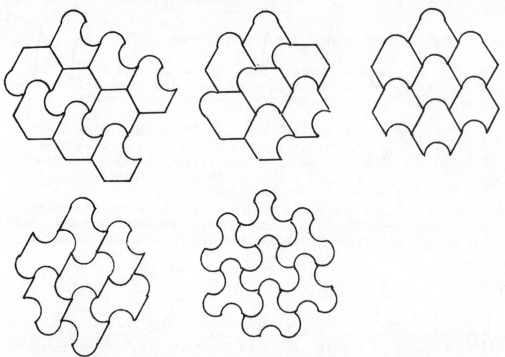

6 D. Following are examples of the different regions required. Note that in addition any region that is the intersection of three half planes could also be the intersection of four or more half planes. One important observation is that the intersection of half planes is always a convex set.

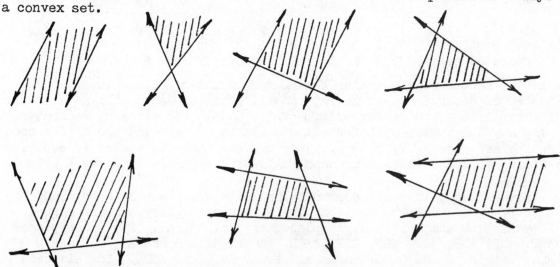

Note that the examples are of the intersection of closed half planes. For this problem the arrangement is more important than distinguishing between open and closed sets.

50.

6 E.　The four point coplanar sets (that are not in five point coplanar
　　　sets) are:　ABLK　　BCML　　CDMN　　DEON　　AEOK
　　　　　　　　ACMK　　BDNL　　CEOM　　DAKN　　EBLO
　　　　　　　　ABMO　　BCNK　　CDOL　　DEKM　　EANL
　　　　　　　　ACNO　　BDOK　　CEKL　　DALM　　EBMN
The three point coplanar sets (that are not in four or five point
coplanar sets) are:　　ABN　　BCO　　CDK　　DEL　　EAM
　　　　　　　　　　　　AMN　　BMO　　CNK　　DKL　　ELM
Students might look for patterns in the listings above.

6 F.　The first two figures are convex; the last two are not.　If
　　　sides adjacent to the semicircle are extended the semicircle
　　　will be contained between them in the first two instances but
not in the second two.　If AB is a side of a polygon and if both angle A
and angle B are less than right angles then side AB can be replaced by
a semicircle with diameter AB.　If either angle A or B is greater than
a right angle then replacement of AB by a semicircle results in a
concave figure.

6 G.　Two more examples of figures are given below.　Note that there are
　　　two different kinds of packing patterns.　In the second example not
　　　all of the figures have the same orientation.　Some copies need to
be turned　in order to fit into the packing.

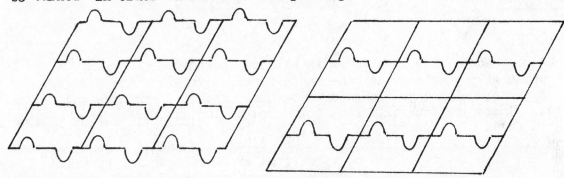

7 A.　The prism table is:

edges in base	3	4	5	6	7	8	9	... N
vertices	6	8	10	12	14	16	18	... 2N
edges	9	12	15	18	21	24	27	... 3N
faces	5	6	7	8	9	10	11	... N+2

The pyramid table is:

edges in base	3	4	5	6	7	8	9	... N
vertices	4	5	6	7	8	9	10	... N+1
edges	6	8	10	12	14	16	18	... 2N
faces	4	5	6	7	8	9	10	... N+1

Every pyramid or prism is such that its vertices and edges constitute a
network in space.　There is always an equivalent network in a plane.
Some examples are:

7 B. The relationship between vertices (V), faces (F) and edges (E)
■   is given by V + F = E + 2. In constructing a plane network each
     edge becomes an arc (A) and each face becomes a region (R). The
corresponding relationship for networks is V + R = A + 2. Note that one
of the faces of the polyhedron corresponds to an unbounded region in
the network. If students need a hint to get them to construct polyhedra
which are neither pyramids nor prisms they can be directed to put two
pyramids or two prisms or a pyramid and a prism together.

7 C. The questions can be answered by experimentation. An argument that
■   does not require experimenting requires a knowledge of the anglesizes
     of the angles of a regular triangle. In degree measure each angle
is 60. If there is a vertex having order two or less there cannot be a
closed surface. If there is a vertex of order six there would be six
triangular faces in the same plane. Again there would not be a closed
surface. More than six triangles having a common vertex results in an
impossible packing situation since N·60 > 360 when N > 6. Therefor, the
only possible orders for vertices are 3, 4 and 5. So there are only
three regular polyhedra having regular triangles for faces. The nets
are drawn below.

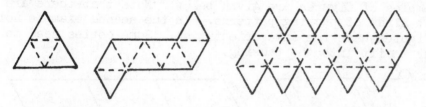

7 D. A polyhedron with five faces is either a pyramid or a prism. A
■   prism with a triangular base has 5 faces, 6 vertices and 9 edges.
     A pyramid with a quadrangular base has 5 faces, 5 vertices and
8 edges. There are four different polyhedra having six faces. A pyramid
having 6 faces has a pentagonal base, 6 vertices and 10 edges. A prism
having six faces has a quadrangular base, 8 vertices and 12 edges. Another
polyhedron with six faces can be visualized as two triangular pyramids
attached at the bases. This figure has 5 vertices and 9 edges. The
fourth polyhedron with six faces has 7 vertices and 11 edges. The figure
has a pentagonal base, three triangular faces and two quadrangular faces.
It looks like a tent.
Examples of polyhedra with seven and eight faces which are neither prisms
nor pyramids are given below.

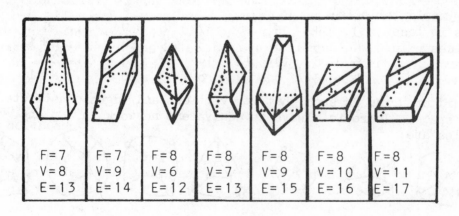

F = 7	F = 7	F = 8	F = 8	F = 8	F = 8	F = 8
V = 8	V = 9	V = 6	V = 7	V = 9	V = 10	V = 11
E = 13	E = 14	E = 12	E = 13	E = 15	E = 16	E = 17

7 E. Each vertex of a square prism is an endpoint for one diagonal of the prism. Since there are eight vertices and each diagonal has two endpoints there must be $8/2 = 4$ diagonals for a square prism. Each vertex of a prism having a regular pentagonal base is an endpoint for two diagonals. Since there are ten vertices and each diagonal has two endpoints there must be $10 \cdot 2/2 = 10$ diagonals for a prism with a regular pentagonal base. Each vertex of a prism having a regular hexagonal base is an endpoint for three diagonals of the prism. There are twelve vertices and each diagonal has two endpoints so there must be $12 \cdot 3/2 = 18$ diagonals in a prism with a regular hexagonal base. Generalizing now, each vertex of a prism having a regular n-gon as base will be an endpoint for n-3 diagonals. Since there are 2n vertices and each diagonal has two endpoints there must be $2n(n-3)/2$ which is $n(n-3)$ diagonals. To consider pyramids we note that segments whose endpoints are base vertices are contained in the base of a pyramid. Segments having one end at a base vertex and the other at the non base vertex are edges. So there are no cases where the segment whose endpoints are vertices can be contained in the interior of a pyramid. So pyramids have no diagonals.

7 F. The relation for V, F and E is $V + F = E + 2$. The relation for A, R and V is $V + R = A + 2$. The network maps are drawn below. Each numeral indicates a color in a coloring of the map.

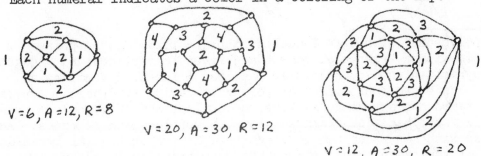

$V = 6, A = 12, R = 8$

$V = 20, A = 30, R = 12$

$V = 12, A = 30, R = 20$

7 G. A pyramid with n edges in the base has n+1 vertices, 2n edges and n+1 faces. Truncation creates another face at each vertex so n+1 new faces are created making the total number of faces $2(n+1)$. Truncation creates three new vertices and deletes one vertex for each of the n base vertices. The net gain is 2n vertices. Truncation creates n new vertices and deletes the non base vertex for a net gain of n-1 vertices. So the truncated pyramid has gained $2n + (n-1) = 3n-1$ vertices. That makes the total number of vertices 4n. Truncation creates three new edges when base vertices are truncated and n new edges when the non base vertex is truncated. The net gain is $n + 3n = 4n$ edges. The total number of edges is 6n. Check to see that $V + F = E + 2$ holds for the truncated pyramid. A prism with n edges in the base has 2n vertices, 3n edges and n+2 faces. Truncation creates another face at each vertex so 2n new faces are created. The total for faces is 3n+2. Truncation deletes each vertex but adds three new vertices for each deleted. The net gain is 4n vertices. The new total for vertices is 6n. Truncation adds three edges for each vertex so 6n edges are added bringing the total number of edges to 9n. Checking to see that $V + F = E + 2$ we have $(3n + 2) + 6n = 9n + 2$.

53.

8 A.   A triangular pyramid will have either a triangle or quadrilateral
       cross section.   A square pyramid will have a cross section which is
       bounded by a triangle, a quadrilateral or a pentagon.   An edge for
a cross section is formed by the intersection of a plane with the face
of the pyramid.   This means there can be no more edges in a cross section
for a pyramid than the pyramid has faces.   By intersecting different
numbers of faces cross sections bounded by polygons having 3, 4, ..., n+1
can be found for pyramids with n-gons for base.

8 B.   A triangular prism will have either a triangle or quadrilateral
       cross section.   A triangular prism has five faces but it is not
       possible to cut all five with the same plane.   A quadrangular
prism will have a cross section bounded by a triangle, a quadrilateral,
a pentagon or a hexagon.   All six faces of a quadrangular prism can be
cut by the same plane so the maximum is possible in this case.

8 C.   The intersection of two half spaces may be a half space, the empty
       set, the interior of a dihedral angle or the strip shown in Figure
       8.18.   The intersection of three half spaces may be a solid half
strip, an "infinite" triangular prism (only three faces) or any figure
that is the intersection of two half spaces.   The intersection of four
half spaces may be an "infinite" quadrangular prism (only four faces)
or a truncated strip.   Pictures of these figures are shown below.

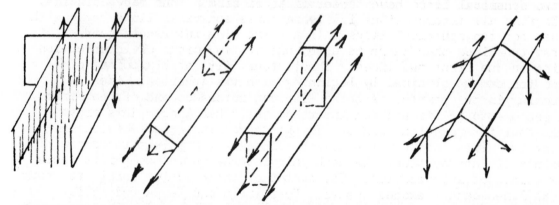

8 D.   Note that the first printing contains an error in Figure 8.19.
       Two copies of the given stack cannot be packed to make a 3 by 3 by 2
       array.   The nine cube stacks are shown below.   Any of them could be
given as an example to get things started.   Note also that the given figures
include only those which are polycubes.(See text p 114).

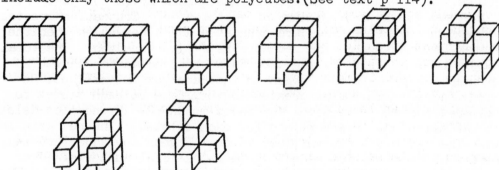

54.

8 E. The number of planes determined can be separated into two types;
■ Those containing the faces of the pyramid and those which do not
contain faces. The n vertices determine n planes which contain
faces. The planes which do not contain faces are determined by endpoints
of a diagonal of the base and the non base vertex. The number of
diagonals in a regular polygon with n-1 edges is $\frac{1}{2}(n-1)(n-4)$. So the
total number is $n+\frac{1}{2}(n-1)(n-4)$. By substitution the number of planes
requested can be found. Students are likely to determine the sequence
7, 11, 16, 22, 29 from the cases assigned and then describe the sequence
in terms of differences.

8 F. Results are contained in the table below.

	Pyramid				Prism			
	AB		AC		AB		AC	
n	P	S	P	S	P	S	P	S
3	1	1	1	1	2	3	3	2
4	2	2	1	2	4	4	4	4
5	1	3	1	3	2	7	5	6
6	2	4	1	4	4	8	6	8
7	1	5	1	5	2	11	7	10
8	2	6	1	6	4	12	8	12

8 G. Two spherical lines can intersect in none, one or two points. If
■ two spherical lines have three points in common then they coincide.
To find all intersections involving three spherical lines begin with
the cases for two spherical lines. If a third line intersects neither of
the first two lines than there is none, one or two points of intersection
depending on the first two lines. Three, four, five or six points of
intersection can be obtained by beginning with two spherical lines
intersecting in two points. A third line can intersect one of the first
two in one or two points and not intersect the other line. This creates
three or four intersection points. If the third line intersects one of
the first two lines in one point and the other in two points there are
five points of intersection. If each pair intersects in two points there
are six points of intersection. The number of intersection points for four
spherical lines cannot exceed twelve. Four lines can be paired in six
ways so two intersection points can be obtained in six ways. The cases
for six to twelve intersections can be illustrated by starting with three
lines intersecting in six points and adding a fourth line to intersect the
others in no points, one point, ... up to six points.

9 A. Two congruent equilateral triangles can be matched in six ways.
■ Two congruent isosceles triangles can be matched in two ways.
Other congruent triangles can be matched in only one way. Two
congruent squares can be matched in eight ways. Two congruent non square
rectangles can be matched in four ways. Two congruent non square rhombuses
can also be matched in four ways. Two congruent parallelograms (not
rhombur or rectangle) can be matched in two ways. Congruent isosceles
trapezoids or congruent kites can also be matched in two ways. Other
congruent quadrilaterals can be matched in only one way. Two congruent
regular pentagons can be matched in ten ways. Two congruent pentagons
having just one line of symmetry can be matched in two ways. Other congruent
pentagons can be matched in just one way.

9 B. The given correspondences are congruence correspondences. All corresponding segments have the same length. There are twelve different congruence correspondences. They are described in the table.

	1	2	3	4	5	6	7	8	9	10	11	12
A	T	V	W	X	Z	Y	X	T	W	V	Y	Z
B	V	W	T	Z	Y	X	Y	W	V	T	Z	X
C	W	T	V	Y	X	Z	Z	V	T	W	X	Y
D	X	Y	Z	T	W	V	T	X	Z	Y	V	W
E	Y	Z	X	W	V	T	V	Z	Y	X	W	T
F	Z	X	Y	V	T	W	W	Y	X	Z	T	Y

9 C. There are twenty-four different positions for the boot shaped polygon. The pictures below identify four different positions. Each picture represents six positions for the polygon. The points marked with an **X** are points where the top of the boot can be moved. Points marked with an **O** are points where the toe of the boot can be moved.

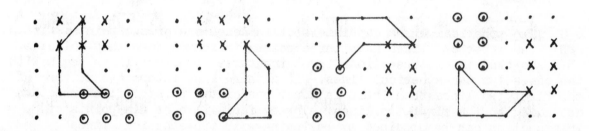

9 D. Cases 2, 3 and 4 are sufficient to conclude that the triangles are congruent. The other cases are not sufficient. In case 1 there may be two triangles which meet the conditions. In case 5 there are infinitely many triangles.

9 E. The points A, Q, M and U are vertices of three noncongruent quadrilaterals. The quadrilaterals are AQMU, AMQU and AMUQ. The five points A, B, C, F and G are vertices for no pentagon. The five points A, C, H, M and F are vertices for one pentagon. The points A, E, H, L, P are vertices for two noncongruent pentagons, AHEPL and AHLPE. The points B, D, H, R, T are vertices for three non congruent pentagons: BHDTR, BHRTD and BRHTD. The points A, D, H, L, P are vertices for four non congruent pentagons. They are ALPDH, AHLPD, ALPHD and ALHPD. The points C, R, T, V, Z are vertices for five pentagons: CVRZT, CRVZT, CVZRT, CVZTR and CVRTZ. The points D, H, L, N, Y are vertices for eight pentagons: DLYNH, DLHNY, DLNHY, DLNYH, DHLNY, DHNLY, DNHLY and DNYLH.

9 F. One strategy is to make tiles with four, then three, then two and then one and finally no blank blocks. Within each group consider the ways to arrange tha blocks. Pictures follow.

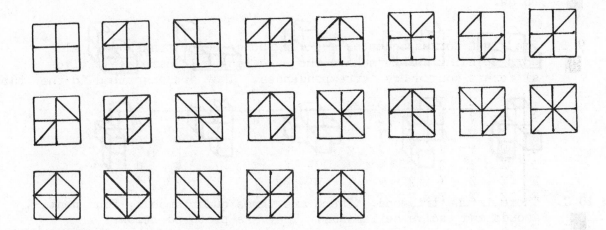

9 G. There are sixteen ways to shade a packing of nine regular triangles when three of them are shaded. The pictures follow.

10 A. There are twelve pentominoes. They are pictured below.

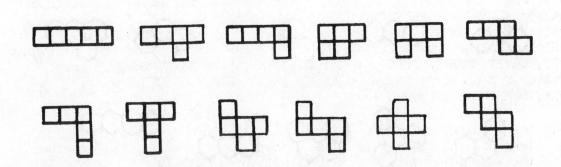

10 B. There are ten pentacubes which are not prisms. They are pictured below.

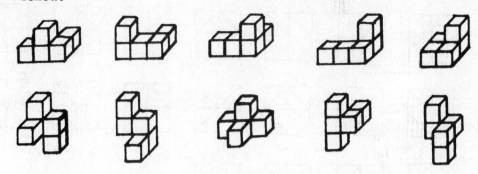

10 C. There is one triamond. There are three quadriamonds, four penti-amonds and twelve hexiamonds. They are pictured below.

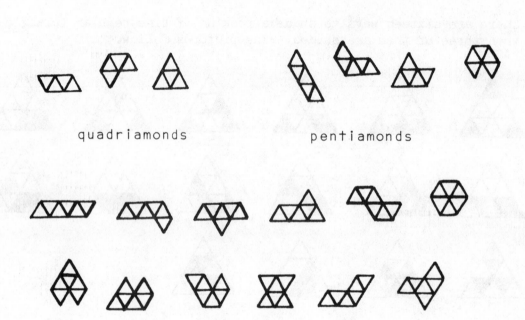

quadriamonds   pentiamonds

hexiamonds

10 D. There are three tricombs. There are seven quadracombs. There are twenty- two pentacombs.

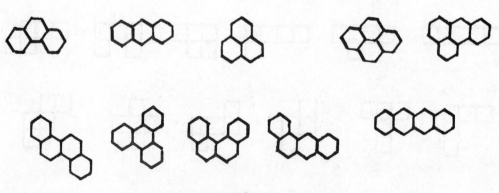

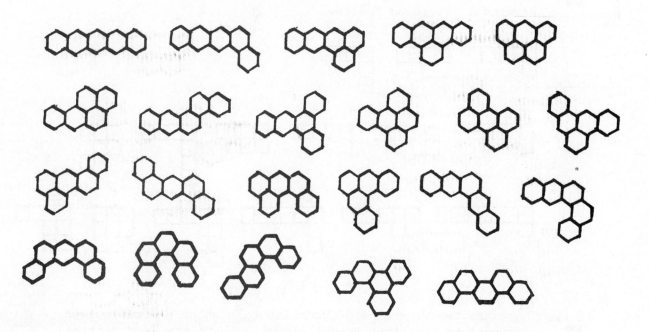

10 E. There are packings of 1, 4, 9, 16, 25, ... regular triangles which
in turn are regular triangles. No polyomino is a triangle; no
polycomb is a triangle. There are many polyominoes which are
quadrilaterals. There are also polyiamonds which are quadrilaterals.
There are no polycombs which are quadrilaterals. There are polyiamonds
which are pentagons. No polyominoes or polycombs are pentagons. There
are polyominoes and polyiamonds which are hexagons. The only polycomb
which is a hexagon is the unicomb. The number of sides in a polyomino
is an even number greater than or equal to four. The number of sides in
a polycomb which is not a unicomb is an even number greater than or
equal to ten. A polyiamond has any number of sides greater than or equal
to three. Some examples are given below.

10 F. There are seven hexacubes that can be constructed by packing the
given square prism with the duocube. Pictures are below.

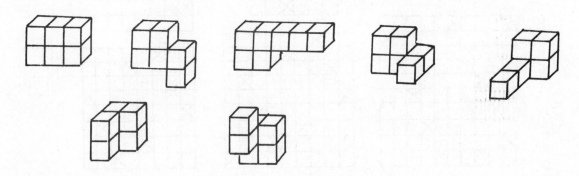

59.

10 G. There are three hexominoes that are hexagons. There are six septom-
inoes that are hexagons. There are seven octominoes that are
hexagons. Pictures follow.

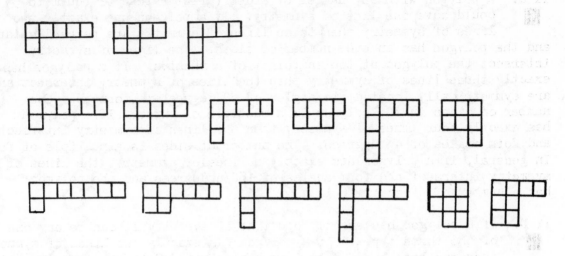

11 A. There are twelve geoboard quadrilaterals which are reflection
congruent to the given quadrilateral. There are four vertical
lines of reflection, three horizontal reflection lines, three
positive slope diagonals and two negative slope diagonals.

11 B. Clearly the number cannot exceed the number of rows or columns.
If two marked squares are in the same row or column they must be
reflection congruent. So the challenge is to find n squares in a
n by n array so that no two are reflection congruent. It isn't hard to
get n squares so that no two are in the same row or column. It is more
difficult to avoid reflection congruence with respect to diagonal lines.
Nevertheless if n is greater than 3 there are n squares on an n by n
array so that no two are reflection congruent. Some solutions appear
below. Students can be encouraged to look for patterns in the solutions.

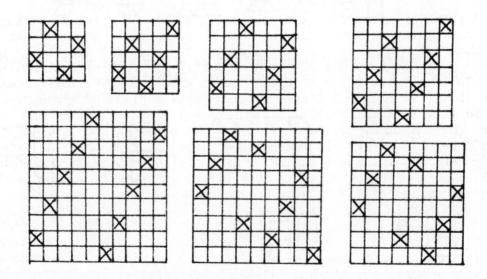

11 C.   A polygon with any number of sides (greater than or equal to 3)
could have one line of symmetry. If a polygon has exactly two
lines of symmetry then these lines of symmetry are perpendicular
and the polygon has an even number of sides. The lines of symmetry
intersect the polygon at the endpoints of a rhombus. If a polygon has
exactly three lines of symmetry then the lines of symmetry intersect and
are symmetrically located (ie angles of 60 degree are formed). The
number of sides in the polygon is a multiple of three. If a polygon
has exactly four lines of symmetry then the lines of symmetry intersect
and form angles of 45 degrees. The number of sides is a multiple of four.
In general, if a polygon has exactly n lines of symmetry, the lines of
symmetry intersect and form angles of 180/n degrees and the polygon
has a number of sides which is a multiple of n.

11 D.   If a polygon has exactly one line of symmetry it can be any one
of the three types. If a polygon has exactly two lines of symmetry
they may both be of type 1 or both of type 2 or one line may be
of type 1 and the other of type2. There can be none of type 3. If a
polygon has exactly three lines of symmetry they must all be of the same
type but all three types are possible. If a polygon has exactly four
lines of symmetry there may be four of type 1 or four of type 2 or there
may be two of type 1 and two of type 2. Some examples are pictured below.

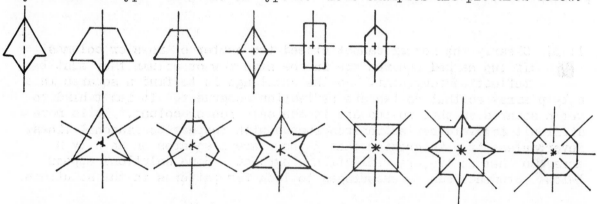

11 E.   A plane of symmetry for a prism will either be parallel to the bases
(and midway between them) or will be parallel to the non base edges.
Each prism has one plane of symmetry of the first type and n planes
of symmetry of the second type. (Assuming a right prism with a regular
base.) So if a prism has n sides in the base and the base is a regular
polygon the prism has n + 1 planes of symmetry. A plane of symmetry for
a pyramid will be determined by the non base vertex and a line of
symmetry for the base. So if a pyramid has n edges in the base and the
base is a regular polygon it will have n planes of symmetry. An exception
to the generalization about planes of symmetry for prisms occurs when the
prism is also a cube. A cube has nine planes of symmetry whereas a non
cube square prism has five planes of symmetry.

11 F.   This problem is similar to problem B in some respects. In problem
B reflection lines with four different slopes need to be considered.
In this problem there are six different slopes for reflection lines.
In the 4 by 4 array the maximum number of triangles is 3. In the 5 by 5

array at most four triangles can be placed so that no two are reflection congruent. In the 6 by 6 array at most six triangles can be located so that no two are reflection congruent. Some arrangements appear below. In constructing arrangements students might be encouraged to mark one triangle and then find all the others which are reflection congruent to it before finding another triangle.

 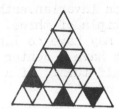 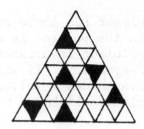

11 G. It is convenient to shade the polygons to denote the two different orientations. One orientation class contains A, C, D, H and J. The remaining polygons, B, E, F, G and I are the other class. If two polygons are in the same class they cannot be reflection congruent. So we need to compare those in one class with those in the other class. The ten reflection congruent pairs are AE, CB, CE, DF, DG, DI, HE, HG, JE and JG. There are six different slopes for reflection lines. A typical reflection line can be drawn by constructing a regular hexagon on the grid and drawing its lines of symmetry. Any reflection line will be parallel to one of those six lines.

12 A. There are three types of turns; half turns, quarter turns clockwise and quarter turns counterclockwise. There are thirty-six geoboard quadrilaterals which are congruent to the given quadrilateral. A picture of the turn centers is shown below.

$\frac{1}{2}$ turn $\frac{1}{4}$ counter $\frac{1}{4}$ clock

12B. For two congruent squares there are either three or four turn centers which can be used to make one coincide with the other. If the sides of one square are parallel to the sides of the other there will be three turn centers, otherwise there will be four. The centers can be found by using the procedure described in 12.2 after the correspondences have been determined. Note that one vertex of one square might be matched with any vertex of the other square. For two congruent regular hexagons there are either five or six turn centers for rotations which will make one coincide with the other. If the sides of the regular hexagons are respectively parallel there will be five centers, otherwise there will be six. The turn centers will be collinear. For two congruent circles there will be infinitely many turn centers for rotations to make them coincide. The turn centers are collinear. The line of turn centers is

62.

the perpendicular bisector of the segment whose endpoints are the centers of the given circles. The generalization is that two regular polygons each having n sides can be made to coincide by means of n-1 or n different rotations. The n-1 occurs when the sides of one are parallel to the sides of the other. All of the turn centers are collinear and the line of turn centers is the perpendicular bisector of the segment whose endpoints are the centers of the given polygons.

12 C. If a polygon has three rotation invariancesthen the number of sides in the polygon is a multiple of three. If a polygon has three rotation invariances it may have no lines of symmetry or three lines of symmetry. It will not have a center of symmetry since none of the invariances involves a half turn. If a polygon has four rotation invariances it has a number of sides which is a multiple of four. It may have no lines of symmetry or four lines of symmetry. It must have a center of symmetry because one of the four invariances must be a half turn. Pictured are some polygons with three rotation invariances.

12 D. (1) Figure 12.6.9 (J) has a vertical axis which contains two vertices. The figure is invariant for quarter turns about this axis. (2) Figure 12.6.9(J) has two horizontal axes which contain midpoints of opposite edges. The figure is invariant for half turns about either axis. (3) Figure 12.6.9 (K) has a vertical axis which contains the midpoints of two faces. The figure is invariant for quarter turns about this axis. (4) Any right pyramid with a base which is a regular polygon has an axis of rotation invariance which contains the center of the base and the non base vertex. The figure is invariant for 1/n turn where n is the number of sides in the base. (5) Construct a polyhedron from a square pyramid and a triangular prism. The non base faces of the prism are to be squares congruent to the base of the pyramid. The square base of the pyramid is attached to one of the square faces of the prism. An axis of rotation invariance will contain the non base vertex of the pyramid and the midpoint of a nonbase edge of the prism. The figure is invariant for half turns about this axis. (6) A right prism with regular triangular bases (like Figure 11.14) has three axes of rotation invariance which contain the midpoint of a non base edge and the midpoint of a non base face. The figure is invariant for half turns about these axes.

12 E. Any two congruent segments are rotation congruent. If they are parallel there is one rotation correspondendence, if not, there are two. Any two rays may or may not be rotation congruent. Two parallel rays are not rotation congruent. If two rays are not parallel there is a unique turn center for a rotation which will make them coincide. Any two lines are rotation congruent. If the lines are parallel then ant point on the line parallel to and midway between the lines is a turn center for the rotation. If the lines intersect than any point on the bisectors of the angles formed by them is a turn center.

12 F.   The set of polygons can be partitioned into two classes according
        to orientation. One class contains A, C, D, H and J and the other
        contains B, E, F, G and I. A member of one class cannot be
rotation congruent to a member of the other class. The rotation congruent
pairs and the amount of clockwise turn from the first figure named to the
second are: AC (2/3), AD ($\frac{1}{2}$), AH (2/3), AJ (5/6), CD (5/6),
CJ (1/6), BI ($\frac{1}{2}$), EF (5/6), EG (2/3), EI (1/3), FG (5/6), FI ($\frac{1}{2}$),
and GI (2/3). There are five different anglesizes for rotation. Students
should check the consistency of the answers by comparing for example
the rotations for AC, CD and AD.

12 G.   Every right pyramid having a regular polygon for a base has an
        axis of rotation invariance which contains the non base vertex
        and the center of the base. The pyramid is rotation invariant for
turns which are multiples of 1/n th of a turn about this axis where n
is the number of edges in the base.

12 H.   Every right prism having regular polygons of n sides as bases
        has an axis of rotation invariance which contains the centers of
        the bases. The prism is rotation invariant for turns which are
1/n th of a turn about this axis. If n is odd each right prism also
has n other axes of rotation invariance. Each of these contains the
midpoint of a non base edge and the center of a non base face. The prism
is rotation invariant for half turns about each of these axes. If n is
even each right prism has n other axes of rotation invariance. n/2 of
these axes contain midpoints of two non base edges. Another n/2 of the
axes contains centers of two non base faces. The prism is rotation
invariant for half turns about each of these axes.

13 A.   The figures that can pack with translation copies are: the two
        quadrilaterals, the first hexagon and the first octagon. The
        other figures can not be packed using translations only. Polygons
with an odd number of edges cannot have the translation packing property.
Polygons with an even number of edges may or may not have the translation
packing property. Although both quadrilaterals given do have the property
they are parallelograms. A general quadrilateral will not have the property.

13 B.   For a start there are twenty-five different vectors whose tail is
        at point A and whose head is at one of the points with letters A
        through Z (there is no letter I). The table below lists these
vectors and the number in each equivalence class.

Vector	#	Vector	#	Vector	#	Vector	#	Vector	#
AA	25	AF	20	AL	15	AQ	10	AV	5
AB	20	AG	16	AM	12	AR	8	AW	4
AC	15	AH	12	AN	9	AS	6	AX	3
AD	10	AJ	8	AO	6	AT	4	AY	2
AE	5	AK	4	AP	3	AU	2	AZ	1

Students might find and discuss the patterns to be found in this table.
You can obtain twent-four more equivalence classes by reversing the order
of head and tail in the above table. The following table considers those

vectors whose tail is at point V. If a vector is equivalent to one in the previous table or its opposite the equivalent from that table is named. If a vector is not equivalent to a vector with head or tail at A the number in the new equivalence class is given.

Vector	*	Vector	*	Vector	*	Vector	*	Vector	*
VV	AA	VQ	FA	VL	LA	VF	QA	VA	VA
VW	AB	VR	16	VM	12	VG	8	VB	4
VX	AC	VS	12	VN	9	VH	6	VC	3
VY	AD	VT	8	VO	6	VJ	4	VD	2
VZ	AE	VU	4	VP	3	VK	2	VE	1

13 C. There can be eleven additional polygons drawn. The twelve polygons (including the given polygon) form a set such that any new polygon congruent to one of the twelve must be translation congruent to one of them. The set of twelve polygons contains two orientation classes with six polygons in each. The six cases correspond to the six angular orientations permitted by the lattice. The number of additional polygons that can be drawn does depend on the starter polygon. For an extreme example if the starter polygon is a regular hexagon then no lattice polygon can be congruent to it without being translation congruent to it. For less extreme examples try a polygon with a single line of symmetry or a polygon with a center of symmetry. A picture of the twelve appears below.

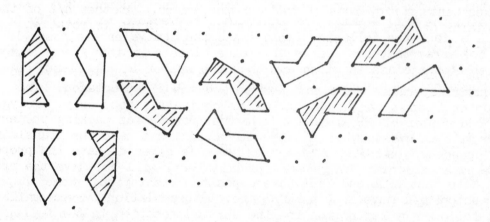

13 D. Counting the given figure as translation congruent to itself there are twelve quadrilaterals that are translation congruent to the given figure. The names of the eleven non zero vectors (using the lettering from Figure 13.14) are: BA, BC, BD, BF, BL, BG, BM, BN, BH, BO, BJ. (Vectors equivalent to these could also be named.) This list starts each vector at B. The endpoints form a 4 by 4 array.

13 E. There can be seven additional polygons drawn. Every lattice polygon which is congruent to the given polygon will be translation congruent to one of the eight polygons. The eight polygons can be partitioned into two orientation classes with four polygons in each class. Each class contains polygons which are rotation congruent to

one another. The number of polygons does depend on the starter polygon.
If the starter is a square then no lattice polygon can be constructed
which is congruent to the square without being translation congruent
to it. If the starter is a non square rectangle then one lattice polygon
can be constructed which is congruent to it without being translation
congruent to it.

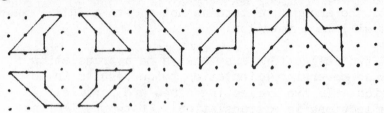

13 F. No examples are given here since examples submitted in response
to the task can be self-checked. If MN is a period vector than
any vector parallel to MN or to NM and whose length is an integral
multiple of either will be a translation invariant vector.

13 G. The sixteen new vectors in the 3 by 3 array are: 1) EG = HK = LN,
2) EK = HN, 3) EM = FN, 4) EN, 5) EL = FM = GN, 6) LF = MG,
7) LK = HG, 8) LG and the opposites of 1) through 8). There are
sixty new vectors in the 4 by 4 array. They are: 1) AD = OR = SV = WZ,
2) AR = OV = SZ, 3) AV = OZ, 4) AZ, 5) AY = BZ, 6) AX = BY = CZ,
7) AW = BX = CY = DZ, 8) WB = XC = YD, 9) WC = XD, 10) WD, 11) WR = SD,
12) WV = SR = OD and their opposites. From this list it should be clear
that there are 24 new equivalence classes; the twelve named and their
opposites. Since there are 60 new vectors it must be that 240 - 60 = 180
vectors in the 4 by 4 array are equivalent to vectors in the 3 by 3
array. In fact the following table lists the equivalence classes in
the 4 by 4 array that are also equivalence classes in the 3 by 3 array.
One member of a class is given and then the number in the class. The
table contains 90 vectors. The other 90 are opposites of these.

AB	12	AS	8	AT	6	WV	6
AC	8	AP	9	AV	4	WQ	4
AO	12	AQ	6	WT	9	WP	6

14 A. Note that EFGD and KJHL have opposite orientation. Some compositions
which will move EFGD to KJHL are: 1) translation by vector GH
followed by reflection in line GH; 2) rotation in DGL followed
by reflection in line LK; 3) reflection in line NG followed by
rotation in GLH. The minimum number of simple transformations required
in a composition which makes EFGD coincide with KJHL is two. The
composition need not contain a rotation (see 1) or a translation (see 2)
but must contain a reflection. A reflection is needed in order to reverse
the orientation. A composition may consist entirely of reflections. For
example reflections in MG followed by FG followed by LK will make EFGD
coincide with KJHL. Note that the discussion for EFGD and MPON should be
different because the figures have the same orientation. A single rotation
can make them coincide. A composition without a rotation which makes them
coincide is reflection in GH followed by reflection in NP. This is also
an example of a composition consisting entirely of reflections. There is
no composition consisting entirely of translations.

14 B.　The composition of two rotations must be a rotation or a
■　　　translation. If the rotations have different turn centers and the
　　　amounts of rotation add to a full turn then the composition will
be a translation. The composition of two half turns is a special case
of this. If two rotations have the same turn center their composition
will be a rotation with the same turn center. If two rotations have
different turn centers and the amounts of turn do not add to a full
turn then the composition will be a rotation.

14 C.　The composition of two reflections must always be a translation
■　　　or a rotation because reversing orientation twice results in no
　　　change in orientation. If two reflecting lines are parallel
the composition of the reflections is a translation. If two reflecting
lines intersect the composition of the reflections is a rotation. Since
the composition of three reflections would reverse orientation the
composition of three reflections can never be a translation or a rotation.
If three reflectin lines are all parallel then the composition of the
three reflections is a single reflection. This includes the case when
there are three reflections but only two lines for the reflections and
the lines are parallel. If there are three distinct lines and they are
not all parallel then the composition of the three reflections will not
be a reflection. Since the composition cannot be a rotation or a
translation either, it follows that some compositions cannot be reduced
to one of the simple transformations.

14 D.　Of the given compositions only the pair involving the composition
■　　　of two translations is a commutative pair. Any two translations
　　　will commute. Two reflections will commute if the reflection lines
are perpendicular or if the two reflections are in the same line.
Two rotations having the same center commute. A reflection and a
translation will commute if the translating vector is parallel to the
relecting line. A reflection and a rotation will commute if the center
of rotation is on the reflecting line. Non trivial translation and
rotations will not commute.

14 E.　Since figure X and figure Y have opposite orientation a composition
■　　　which makes them coincide must contain a reflection. Types iv
　　　and vi contain a single reflection. The other four types will not
reverse orientation. Since X and Z are of opposite orientation a
composition of type iv or vi is also required in order to make them
coincide, The same is true for X and W. Figures Y and Z have the same
orientation so they cannot be made to coincide using transformation
types iv or vi. Transformation types i, ii and iii are possible. Type v
is not possible unless the rotation is a multiple of a full turn. (No
specific compositions are given here. Compositions proposed by students
need to be checked individually.)

14 F.　Finding two translations is easy. You can select any translation
■　　　for the first translation. Say you choose a translation which
　　　moves figure P to P'. Then P' and Q are translation congruent.
To name the second translaion choose a point of P' and the corresponding
point of Q to name the vector. Finding two rotations is fairly easy.
Choose any center and any positive amount of turn less than a full turn.

Perform the rotation to move figure P to P'. Now P' and Q are rotation
congruent. You need to find the turn center. You do this by finding
two points A', B' on P' and the corresponding points A, B on Q. The
turn center is the intersection of the perpendicular bisectors of AA'
and BB'. If X is the point of intersection then A'XA is the angle of
rotation desired for the second rotation. There is not quite so much
freedom in finding two reflections. Begin by locating a point H of P
and the corresponding point H' of Q. Select any line which is perpendicular to segment HH' and call it m. Reflect P in line m to obtain P'.
Now P' and Q are reflection congruent. The reflection line is the
perpendicular bisector of the segment whose endpoints are H' and the
reflection of H in line m.

14 G.   (Note there may be a misprint in line 1 of p 171. The word should
        be "reflection" instead of "translation".)
        If the reflection is to be done first begin by choosing a point A
of one figure P and the corresponding point A' of the other figure Q.
Let m be the perpendicular bisector of the segment AA'. Then reflect
P in line m to obtain P'. Now P' and Q are rotation congruent and the
center of the rotation is A'. The amount of turn is angle B'A'B where
B' is on P' and B is the corresponding point of Q. If the rotation is
to be done first begin by choosing a point A of one figure P and the
corresponding point A' of the other figure Q. Let M be the midpoint of
AA'. Then rotate P a half turn about M to obtain P'. The figures P'
and Q are reflection congruent. The reflection line can be found to be
the perpendicular bisector of corresponding points of figures P' and Q.
The reflection line will contain A'.

14 H.   The composition of a translation and a reflection can be
        equivalent to a single reflection if the translating vector
        is perpendicular to the line of reflection. The composition of
a translation and a reflection can never be equivalent to a single
translation or a single rotation because the latter transformations
preserve orientation whereas the composition does not. The composition
of a rotation and a reflection can be equivalent to a single reflection
if the turn center is on the reflection line. The single reflection is
in a line through the turn center. An example which is easy to construct
has a figure X and a line m and a point C on m. Rotate X a half turn
about C, then reflect the rotation in m. The resulting figure is
reflection congruent to X and the reflection line is perpendicular to m
at C. (Note this is a variation of the composition of two reflections
in intersecting lines problem).

15 A.   One plan is to produce ratchet polygons. To produce a ratchet
        polygon with n rotation invariances, construct a regular n-gon and
        replace half of each edge with two edges which form the ratchet.
Another plan is to choose a figure that does not ahve any line of symmetry
and rotate it 1/n th of a turn and all multiples of 1/n. Some examples
follow.

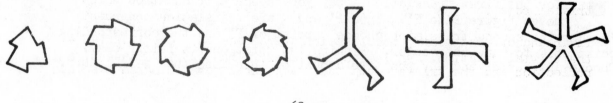

15 B. The composition table for an equilateral triangle is given in
Figure 15.7. The table is not commutative. For example the
reflection in k does not commute with the rotation of 2/3 turn.
Following is a composition table for a square. The numerals 0, 1, 2, 3
represent turns of 0/4, 1/4, 2/4 and 3/4 respectively. The letters
k, l, m, n represent reflections in lines k, l, m and n.

	0	1	2	3	k	l	m	n
0	0	1	2	3	k	l	m	n
1	1	2	3	0	n	k	l	m
2	2	3	0	1	m	n	k	l
3	3	0	1	2	l	m	n	k
k	k	l	m	n	0	1	2	3
l	l	m	n	k	3	0	1	2
m	m	n	k	l	2	3	0	1
n	n	k	l	m	1	2	3	0

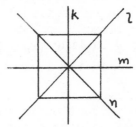

The composition table for a regular polygon can be partitioned into four
parts similar to those in the table for the square. A regular n-gon will
have a table where one corner is an n by n array of rotations composed
with rotations resulting in single rotations. There are two n by n arrays
of rotations composed with reflections to get reflections. There is
another n by n array of reflections composed with reflections to obtain
rotations. A rectangle that is not a square is an example of a figure
which has both rotation and reflection invariances but the table is
unlike that of a regular polygon.

15 C. Figures A and D have two rotations and two reflection invariances.
Figures B and F have one rotation and one reflection invariance.
Figures C and E have three rotations and no reflection invariances.
There are five other types that can be constructed on the given lattice.
They are: one rotation and no reflections, two rotations and no reflections
six rotations and no reflections, three rotations and three reflections,
six rotations and six reflections. Examples of these follow.

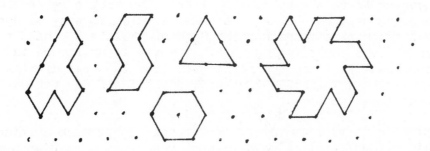

15 D. Triangles may have one, two or six invariances. If one invariance
it is the trivial rotation. A scalene triangle is an example. If
there are two invariances one is a reflection, the other the
trivial rotation. An isosceles triangle is an example. If six invariances
the triangle is regular. There are three rotation and three reflection
invariances. The most general quadrilateral has only one invariance,
the trivial rotation. An isosceles trapezoid has two invariances, a
reflection and the trivial rotation. A general parallelogram also has

69.

two invariances; both are rotations. A non square rhombus has two reflections and two rotations. A non square rectangle has the same four invariances. A square has eight invariances; four are rotations and four are reflections. A pentagon may have one, two or ten invariances. If one invariance it is the trivial rotation. A general pentagon is an example. If two invariances they must be a reflection and the trivial rotation. A regular pentagon has ten invariances consisting of five rotations and five reflections.

15 E. There are twelve different invariances. The correspondences are given in the following table.

	1	2	3	4	5	6	7	8	9	10	11	12
T	T	V	W	X	Z	Y	T	W	V	X	Y	Z
V	V	W	T	Z	Y	X	W	V	T	Y	Z	X
W	W	T	V	Y	X	Z	V	T	W	Z	X	Y
X	X	Y	Z	T	W	V	X	Z	Y	T	V	W
Y	Y	Z	X	W	V	T	Z	Y	X	V	W	T
Z	Z	X	Y	V	T	W	Y	X	Z	W	T	V

1 is trivial rotation
2 is 1/3 turn about k
3 is 2/3 turn about k
4 is ½ turn about l
5 is ½ turn about m
6 is ½ turn about n
7 is reflection in plane through TX
8 is reflection in plane through VY
9 is reflection in plane through WZ
10 is reflection in plane parallel to bases
11 is 2 followed by 10
12 is 3 followed by 10

There are six rotations, four reflections and two compositions which are neither rotations nor reflections.

	1	2	3	4	5	6	7	8	9	10	11	12
1	1	2	3	4	5	6	7	8	9	10	11	12
2	2	3	1	5	6	4	8	9	7	11	12	10
3	3	1	2	6	4	5	9	7	8	12	10	11
4	4	6	5	1	3	2	10	12	11	7	9	8
5	5	4	6	2	1	3	11	10	12	8	7	9
6	6	5	4	3	2	1	12	11	10	9	8	7
7	7	9	8	10	12	11	1	3	2	4	6	5
8	8	7	9	11	10	12	2	1	3	5	4	6
9	9	8	7	12	11	10	3	2	1	6	5	4
10	10	11	12	7	8	9	4	5	6	1	2	3
11	11	12	10	8	9	7	5	6	4	3	1	2
12	12	10	11	9	7	8	6	4	5	2	3	1

Students might look for patterns in the table. Note that the composition of two reflections is a rotation and the composition of two rotations is a rotation. Invariances 11 and 12 cannot be described as simple rotations or reflections.

15 F. An octagon may have one, two, four, eight or sixteen invariances.
The patterns are given below.

15 G. If the reflection in Q_m is followed by the reflection in Q_k the
composition is R_t where $t \equiv 2(m-k)$ (mod 12). For example,
if reflection in Q_7 is followed by reflection in Q_3 the composition
is equivalent to R_8. Note $2(7-3) = 2 \cdot 4 = 8$. If the order of the
reflections is reversed we find $2(3-7) = 2(-4) = -8$. But $-8 \equiv 4$ mod 12,
so the composition is equivalent to a clockwise turn of $4/12$.
If the polygon had 360 sides then $t \equiv 2(m-k)$ mod 360.

16 A. Vector AB is a period vector. T_{XY} is a translation invariance
for the figure whenever XY is collinear with AB and the length
of XY is a multiple of the length of AB. The lines in the figure
below are reflection invariant lines.

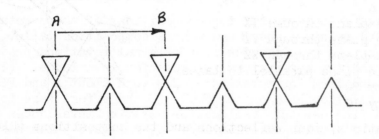

16 B. All examples are possible. 1 is not rotation invariant and not
reflection invariant. 2 is rotation invariant but not reflection
invariant. 3 is reflection invariant but not rotation invariant.
4 is both reflection and rotation invariant. When there are reflection
or rotation invariances there must be infinitely many of them unless
the reflection line is parallel to the period vector.

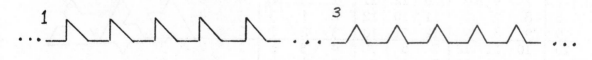

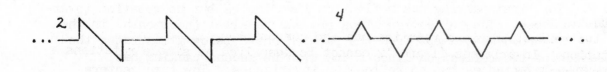

71.

16 **C.** The patterns will be the same regardless of the point chosen
as origin. The pattern in all of these cases will be the same
as a parallelogram lattice. In the first case the parallelogram
is not a square. In the last two cases the parallelogram is a square.
In the figures below four lattice points are labelled A, B, C and D.

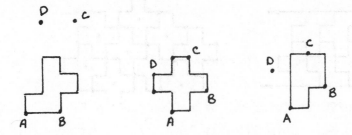

16 **D.** The pattern for half turns is $H_m \circ H_n = T_{2(m-n)}$. The composition
of half turns is not commutative since $m-n \neq n-m$ for all integers
m and n. The pattern for composing half turns and translations
is $H_n \circ T_m = H_{n-\frac{1}{2}m}$ and $T_m \circ H_n = H_{n+\frac{1}{2}m}$. The composition is not commutative.
Note that the figure is rotation invariant about points that are identified
with halves of integers as well as points that are identified with integers.

16 **E.** Suppose points A and B are points and a figure is invariant with
respect to R_{A1}, R_{A2}, R_{B1}, R_{B2} (ie 1/3 and 2/3 turn about A and B.)

Then the figure is invariant for compositions of these rotations.
Draw some figure and points A and B and make a composition table. The
table shown below should result. The four original rotations produce
four translations and two new centers for rotation invariance. (In the
table A2 is shortened form for rotation of 2/3 turn about A and FB is
short form for translation with vector FB.) If the effort were to be
continued we would find new turn centers for rotation invariances at
all lattice points of a triangular lattice. So a figure which has two
turn centers and is rotation invariant with respect to thirds of a turn
will have infinitely many rotation invariances and the centers will form
a triangular lattice. A figure is shown which when extended has the
properties required.

	A1	A2	B1	B2
A1	A2	A0	C2	FB
A2	A0	A1	AG	D2
B1	D2	BF	B2	B0
B2	CD	C2	B0	B1

16 **F.** The first packing has reflection invariances but no rotation invariances. The reflection lines are all parallel (horizontal in the
figure.) An exerpt from the packing shown below illustrates the
location of two reflection lines m and n. The second packing has
rotation invariances but no reflection invariances. The turn centers

72.

form a square lattice. The packing is invariant with respect to 1/4,
1/2 and 3/4 turns for each turn center. An exerpt from the packing
illustrates the pattern of the centers. The third packing has no
reflection invariances and not rotation invariances (except of course
for the trivial rotation.)

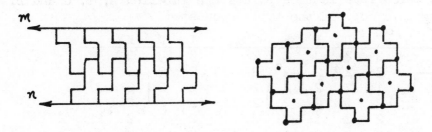

16 G. Other points of the figure can be located by composing reflections.
        The other points are points of a hexagonal lattice. The twelve
        points obtained from all of the double reflections are the vertices
for a packing of three regular hexagons about a point. Triple reflections
form a ring of points about these hexagonal vertices.

17 A. With two copies a polygon with three, four, five or six sides
       can be constructed. The maximum number of sides is six. With
       three copies a polygon can be constructed having four, five, six
seven, eight or nine sides. With four copies the minimum number of sides
in a polygon is three and the maximum is twelve. All numbers of sides
between the minimum and the maximum are possible to construct. With an
even number of pieces the polygon with the minimal number of sides has
three sides. With an odd number of pieces that minimal number is four.
The maximal number of sides is three times the number of pieces. All
numbers of sides between the minimal and maximal number are possible.
Pictures for three and four pieces are shown below.

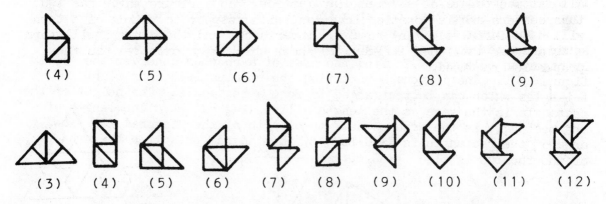

17 B. Results will vary depending on the group tested and the skill of
       the examiner. This is a good project for students who have access
       to subjects even if it is just one or two subjects. Some students
will not believe the results unless they see it for themselves.

17 C. Same comment as for problem 17B.

Responses will differ depending on the manner in which the partitions are constructed. If B is a tangram rearrangement of two tangram pieces of A and if C is a tangram rearrangement of two tangram pieces of B then C is a tangram rearrangement of two, three or four tangram pieces of A. As the number of pieces in the rearrangements change this pattern can emerge. If B is a tangram rearrangement of n tangram pieces of A and if C is a tangram rearrangement of m pieces of B then C is a tangram rearrangement of at most n·m pieces of A.

17 E. Following is a copy of the table requested.

	A	B	C	D	E	F	G	H	I	J	K	L
A	1	2	2	2	3	2	2	2	3	3	3	3
B	2	1	2	2	2	2	2	2	2	3	2	2
C	2	2	1	2	2	2	2	2	2	2	2	2
D	2	2	2	1	2	2	2	2	2	2	2	2
E	3	2	2	2	1	2	2	2	2	3	2	2
F	2	2	2	2	2	1	2	2	2	3	2	2
G	2	2	2	2	2	2	1	2	2	3	2	3
H	2	2	2	2	2	2	2	1	2	2	2	3
I	3	2	2	2	2	2	2	2	1	2	2	2
J	3	3	2	2	3	3	3	2	2	1	3	3
K	3	2	2	2	2	2	2	2	2	3	1	2
L	3	2	2	2	2	2	3	3	2	3	2	1

Most of the entries are "2". Pentominoes C and D are most "like" the others in the sense that any pentomino can be made from two pieces of either C or D. Pentomino J is the least "like" the others in the sense that seven of the other eleven pentominoes require three pieces from J in order to make them.

17 F. The given curve can be partitioned into five tangram pieces. Three of these pieces are diagonals of the unit square. The other two pieces are diagonals of a 1 by 2 rectangle. To construct a curve with the same length as Figure 17.15 construct curves that are tangram rearrangements of the five pieces described.

17 G. The packing is shown in the picture below. The tangramprinciple establishes that the area inside the large square is the sum of the areas inside the other two squares. These squares are squares on the edges of a right triangle. The conclusion is the Pythagorean relation. To find the area of a rhombus consider the figure ABCD. The diagonals partition the rhombus into four right triangles which can be rearranged to form a rectangle. The height of the rectangle is the same as the length of the diagonal BD. The length of the rectangle is the same as half the length of the diagonal AC. The area of the rectangle is $\frac{1}{2}$·AC·BD. By the tangram principle the area of the rhombus is also $\frac{1}{2}$·AC·BD.

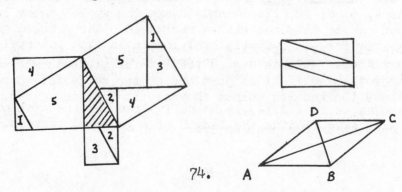

18 A.   Refer to Figure 13.14 pg 154 of the text for letter labels on the
        geoboard. The following table uses that scheme.

Endpoints	AB	AC	AG	AD	AH	AE	AN	AJ	AK	AQ	AP	AT	AU	AZ
Distance	1	2	2	3	3	4	4	4	5	5	6	6	7	8
# of paths	1	1	2	1	3	1	6	4	5	10	15	20	35	70

Two distinct points will be a distance of one, two, three, four, five,
six, seven or eight units apart. The table gives examples of distances
and also the number of "direct" paths from one point to another. It may
be discovered that knowing how many paths from A to Q and A to S can
help to find the number of paths from A to T. If you choose two points
from the set containing A, C, E, G, J, L, N, P, R, T, V, X, Z, a
maximum path of 24 units can be constructed using the chosen points as
endpoints. If two points are chosen from the complimentary set then
a maximum path of 22 units can be constructed from one chosen point
to the other. A path of length 23 is the maximal if the path must
connect a point from one set with a point in the other set.

18 B.   The honor roll of longest poygons is given below. The longest
        triangle is $8 + 4\sqrt{2}$ which is approximately 13.64 units. It is a
4 by 4 right triangle.

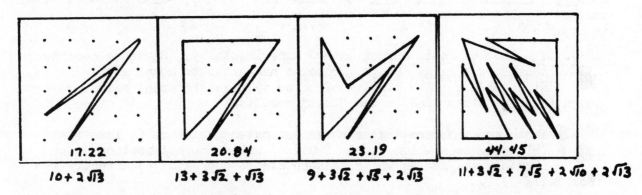

17.22	20.84	23.19	44.45
$10 + 2\sqrt{13}$	$13 + 3\sqrt{2} + \sqrt{13}$	$9 + 3\sqrt{2} + \sqrt{5} + 2\sqrt{13}$	$11 + 3\sqrt{2} + 7\sqrt{5} + 2\sqrt{10} + 2\sqrt{13}$

18 C.   Let n be the number of sides in a regular polygon. If n is even
        the number of diameters is $\frac{1}{2}$n. If n is odd the number of diameters
        is n. When n is even each vertex is an endpoint for one diameter.
When n is odd each vertex is an endpoint for two diameters. All
diameters are also diagonals except when n 3. For regular triangles
the diameters are the edges.

18 D.   There are very many different lengths for quadrilaterals. The
        lengths 4, 6, 8, 10, 12, 14 and 16 are the whole number lengths
        and each can be attained with a rectangle. The problem can be
modified by asking for one quadrilateral length in each interval (n , n+1)
for n between 4 and 17 inclusive. The problem could even ask for one
quadrilateral in each interval (n , n+ 2) for odd n between 3 and 17.
Another variation is to find as many lengths as possible in a smaller
interval, for example in (12,14). The motivation for the problem is
to provide practice in finding the length of a geoboard polygon.

18 E. The theoretical values will be given here for comparison with
measurements obtained by students. The measure of an n-gon
using the apothem as unit is 2n·tan(180/n) for n = 3, 4, 5, ...
and for tangent arguments in degrees. This relation can be derived by
examining a right triangle having the apothem as one leg and half an
edge as the other leg. The approximate lengths are as follows:

n	3	4	5	6	...	12
length	10.2	8	7.3	6.8	...	6.43

As a regular polygon increases in number of edges it approaches a
circle and the apothem approaches a radius. As n increases the length
of an n-gon should approach 2π when the apothem is used as a unit.

18 F. Examples of geoboard polygons for p, q, r, s and t are given
below. The maximum value for u is 2 and can be realized by a
parallelogram.

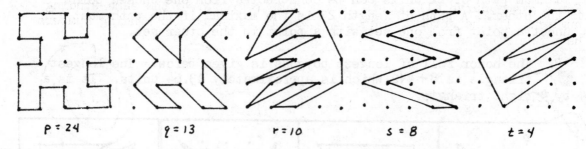

p = 24   q = 13   r = 10   s = 8   t = 4

18 G. The problem is to approximate π experimentally. Students need to
construct a large enough circle to make results meaningful.
Students might try circles of three to five different sizes
and note which sizes produce the "best" results.

19 A. There are sixteen angles whose estimated anglesize is less than
thirty degrees which can be found by using the subtraction
strategy and angles whose measure can be approximated directly
from Table 19.1.

Angle	Approx	Subtr	Angle	Approx	Subtr	Angle	Approx	Subtr
WAR	4	76-72	WAY	24	76-53	MAG	18	63-45
RAM	9	72-63	RAY	19	72-53	SAG	11	56-45
WAM	13	76-63	MAY	10	63-53	YAG	8	53-45
WAS	20	76-56	SAY	3	56-53	MAU	26	63-37
RAS	16	72-56	RAG	27	72-45	MAO	29	63-34
MAS	7	63-56						

19 B. There is no largest anglesize for angles in a triangle. The
measures of anglesize for angles in a triangle are bounded above
by 180 degrees. There is no largest anglesize for angles in polygons
that are not triangles. These measures are bounded above by 360 degrees.
There is no smallest anglesize for angles in any polygon. The lower limit
for anglesize is 0 degrees. The sum of degree measures of the angles of
a triangle is 180 degrees. For a quadrilateral the sum is 360 and for
an n-gon the sum is (n-2)·180. For regular n-gons each angle has degree
measure (n-2)·180/n. A table summarizing other results follows.

	acute	obtuse	right	reflex
triangle	2,3	0,1	0,1	0
quadrilateral	0,1,2,3	0,1,2,3	0,1,2,4	0,1
pentagon	0 to 4	0 to 5	0,1,2,3	0,1,2
hexagon	0 to 5	0 to 6	0 to 5	0 to 3
n-gon	*	0 to n	*	0 to n-3

For $n \geq 6$ the number of right angles or acute angles must be less than $(2/3)(n+2)$. If right angles or acute angles exceed this number then the remaining angles would have to exceed 360 degrees each.

19 C. If a point is in the interior of a simple closed curve the winding number of the curve about the point is either 1 or -1 depending on the orientation of the curve. If a point is in the exterior of a simple closed curve the winding number of the curve about the point is zero regardless of the orientation of the curve. For a given curve all points in the same region have the same winding number. If the orientation of a curve is reversed the winding numbers have their signs reversed.

    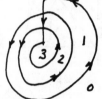

19 D. Keep segment XY fixed in Figure 19.17. The degree measures of angles possible to construct are as follows:

Angle XPR_1 for the various S

S_1	S_2	S_3	S_4	S_5	S_6	S_7
120	105	90	75	60	45	30

Angle XPR_2 for the various S

S_1	S_2	S_3	S_4	S_5	S_6	S_7
135	120	105	90	75	60	45

Anglesizes for XPR_3 will be similar to those for XPR_1. Changing from one peg to an adjacent peg seems to change the degree measure of the angle by 15. The table contains sizes from 30 to 135 in increments of 15. Students might try to find anglesizes of 15, 150 and 165 by moving X and Y. An angle of 150 degrees can be obtained using chords R_1R_3 and XR_2. Angles of 15 and a65 degrees are impossible. The generalization is the measure of the angle formed by two chords is half the sum of the measures of the intercepted arcs.

19 E. For reference consider the 12-point circle labelled from the top clockwise from A to M, skipping letter I. Anglesizes of 15 to 120 degrees in increments of 15 can be obtained. Examples appear in the table below. The general pattern is that angle P is half the difference of the measures of the intercepted arcs.

Points	AB & CD	AB & DE	AB & EF	AB & FG
Angle	120	90	60	30

Points	AC & DE	AC & EF	AC & FG	AC & HG
Angle	105	75	45	15

19 F. One strategy for getting differences in triangle anglesize as low as possible is to try to construct angles close to 60 degrees. Use the tangent table or either addition or subtraction strategies to help. In a regular pentagon each anglesize is 108 degrees. To get the difference in anglesize as low as possible try to construct angles whose measures are close to 108 degrees. Note that the number of such angles you can draw in a single polygon is restricted on a 5 by 5 geoboard. The problem can be extended by asking if you can do a better job with a 6 by 6 or with a 7 by 7 geoboard. Some pictures appear below.

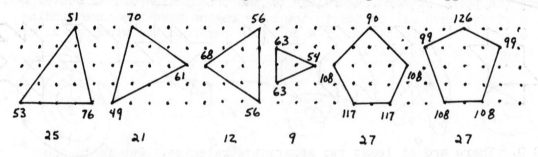

25   21   12   9   27   27

20 A. If b represents the number of boundary pegs and i represents the number of interior pegs associated with a geoboard polygon then the area A is given by $A = i + \frac{1}{2}b - 1$. The unit of area is the area of the smallest geoboard square. This formula is not limited to a 5 by 5 geoboard but applies to any lattice polygon.

20 B. The table which follows gives the maximum areas for polygons on a 5 by 5 geoboard. There is a pattern of three successive polygons having the same maximal area for four entries in the table. After that point the size of the board forces a change in the pattern.

# sides	3	4	5,6,7	8,9,10	11,12,13	14,15,16
max area	8	16	$15\frac{1}{2}$	15	$14\frac{1}{2}$	14

The minimal area for polygons on a geoboard is given by $A = \frac{1}{2}(n-2)$ where n is the number of sides in the polygon. Examples are constructed by drawing polygons with no interior pegs. See problem 20A and derive the relation using b = 0.

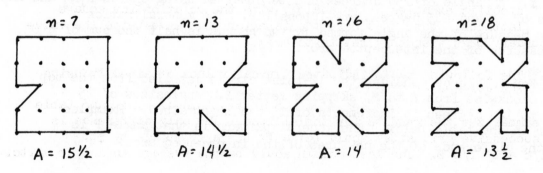

78.

20 C. If a geoboard polygon has an area of 7 the number of edges can
be no more than 16. This can be demonstrated by using the relation
$A = i + \frac{1}{2}b - 1$ where $A = 7$. Then $i + \frac{1}{2}b = 8$. Since $i \geq 0$ it must be
that $b \leq 16$. There are polygons having area 7 for all numbers of edges
from 3 through 16 inclusive. In order to find examples it is helpful
to think in terms of the number of boundary pegs and interior pegs
needed to produce an area of 7. In the examples that follow $b = n$
when n is even and $b = n + 1$ when n is odd.

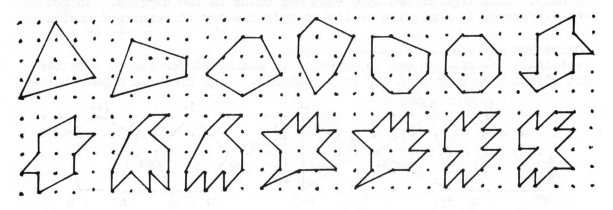

20 D. There are at least two apparent strategies. One is to use
$A = i + \frac{1}{2}b - 1$ when $A = 4$ to produce these combinations for b
and i: $b = 4$ and $i = 3$, $b = 6$ and $i = 2$, $b = 8$ and $i = 1$, $b = 10$
and $i = 0$. It is impossible to draw a triangle in the last of
these four cases. There are triangles for the other four cases. The
other strategy is to find factors of 8 which are possible lengths for
base and height. They must also be geoboard lengths. Possible factor
pairs are: 4 and 2, 2 and 4, $\sqrt{8}$ and $\sqrt{8}$, $4\sqrt{2}$ and $\sqrt{2}$, $\sqrt{2}$ and $4\sqrt{2}$. The
last case is impossible. Triangles can be constructed for the other
cases. Pictures of eight triangles with area 4 follow.

20 E. The relationship is $A = 2i + b - 2$. This can be discovered from
specific examples or by analogy with the relation for square
lattices. Note that here too interior pegs have twice the value
of boundary pegs when they relate to area.

20 F. The following table indicates typical values obtained by using
the average of inner and outer measures. When the grid size
gets near 1/8 r a value close to π is obtained. The same table
also summarizes the results for the ellipse. The only difference is
that successive grid sizes would be: a by b, $\frac{1}{2}a$ by $\frac{1}{2}b$, $\frac{1}{4}a$ by $\frac{1}{4}b$,
and 1/8 a by 1/8 b. The last column would be the average in a by b units.

grid size	inner	outer	average	avg in r-units	
r	0	4	2	2/1	2
$\frac{1}{2}$r	4	16	10	10/4	2.5
$\frac{1}{4}$r	32	60	46	46/16	2.875
1/8 r	172	232	202	202/64	3.16

20 G.   Suppose triangle ABC has base AB. Segments interior to the
triangle and perpendicular to AB are chosen. An average length
is determined. This average is multiplied by AB to approximate the
area. The true average of the segments is half the length of the altitude
to edge AB. For a parallelogram choose segments perpendicular to a
diagonal and then follow the procedure for triangles. For a trapezoid
choose segments perpendicular to the longer base. In estimating the
area of the circle in Figure 20.15 I drew 10 vertical segments and measured
each in millimeters obtaining 30, 40, 46, 50, 51, 48, 43, 36, 50, 19.
The average is 41.3 which is rounded to 41. This average is multiplied
by the diameter in millimeters which is 51. The product is 2091 which is
rounded to 2100. In estimating the area of the ellipse I drew ten
vertical segments and measured each in millimeters to obtain: 24, 32, 38,
41, 43, 44, 43, 41, 35, 18. The average is 30.3 which is rounded to 30.
The average is multiplied by 2a which is 62 millimeters. The product is
1860 which is rounded to 1900. The true measure of the area of the
circle is in the interval (2000,2100). The true measure of the area of
the ellipse is in the interval (2100, 2200). This method gives fairly
good estimates if enough segments are used in the average or if those
chosen are really representative.

21 A.   To find either the top or the bottom surface area from an array
simply count the number of nonzero entries in the array. To find
either the front or back surface area add the numerals in the
front row and add the excess from row to row. To find either the right
or left surface area add the numerals in the right column and add the
excess from column to column. For example consider the array in Figure
21.11. There are ten nonzero entries in the array so the top surface
area is 10 and the bottom surface area is 10. The front row sum is
2 + 0 + 1 + 0 = 3. The excess from the next row to the front row is 1 + 4 + 2 + 0
which is 7. The excess in the next pair of rows is 0 + 0 + 0 + 2 = 2. The
excess in the last pair of rows is 0 + 0 + 0 + 0 = 0. The total is 3 + 7 + 2 + 0
which is 12. So the front and back surface area are each 12. The right
column sum is 0 + 0 + 2 + 0 = 2. The excess from the next column to the
right column is 1 + 3 + 0 + 0 = 4. The excess from the next pair of columns is
0 + 1 + 0 + 1 = 2. The excess in the last pair of columns is 2 + 0 + 0 + 0 = 2.
The total is 2 + 4 + 2 + 2 = 10. So the right and left surface areas are
each 10. The total surface area is 2(10 + 12 + 10) = 2(32) = 64. The surface
areas of the remaining stacks are given with top, front and then right
surface areas.

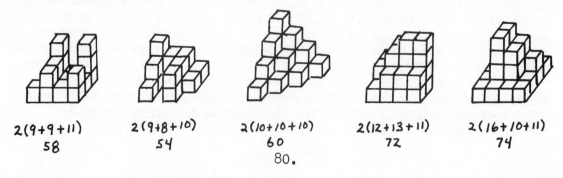

2(9+9+11)   2(9+8+10)   2(10+10+10)   2(12+13+11)   2(16+10+11)
   58   54   60   72   74

80.

21 B. There are several arrangements of fifteen block stacks which
have a surface area of 40. One of them is shown below. Forty
appears to be the minimum. Note that the surface area must be
an even number if the blocks must be stacked face to face. The maximum
surface area for a fifteen block stack is 62. One arrangement for a
maximal stack is a 1 by 1 by 15 stack. Many others are possible. One
figure given below has a surface area of 60. By removing the block on
the left and placing it in the top row (third from right) the surface
area is reduced by two. Surface areas that are even numbers from 60 to
50 can be obtained in this way. The other examples shown below are
arrangements with areas 44, 46 and 48. So all even numbers from 40 to
62 inclusive are possible surface areas for a fifteen block stack. A
stack of twelve blocks would have a surface area which is an even number
from 32 to 50 inclusive. A stack of n blocks stacked as a polycube
can have a maximum area of $4n+2$.

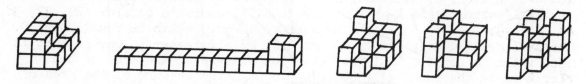

21 C. The surface area of a sphere is given by $S = 4\pi r^2$ where r is
the length of the radius. The volume of a sphere is given by
$V = 4/3 \pi r^3$ where r is again the length of the radius. So the
desired ratios are $S/r^2 = 4\pi$ and $V/r^3 = 4/3 \pi$. The results obtained
will depend on the segments and circles chosen.

21 D. The inner and outer measure can be estimated from the grid. The
inner measure is $8^2 + 8^2 + 6^2 + 6^2 + 4^2 + 4^2 + 2^2 + 2^2 + 0^2 + 0^2 = 240$.
Outer measure is $10^2 + 10^2 + 8^2 + 8^2 + 6^2 + 6^2 + 4^2 + 4^2 + 2^2 + 2^2 = 440$.
The average of the inner and outer measures is 340. This estimate
compares favorably with the computed value of 1000/3.

21 E. This problem can help students distinguish between volume and surface
area. To gain altitude and to create volume the surface area has
to be diminished. The greatest volume for a cone with a slant
height of 10 cm is approximately 403 cubic cm. Experimentally derived
values are expected to differ from this. The greatest volume occurs
when the radius is about 8.2 cm and the altitude is about 5.8 cm. The
surface area can be computed in two pieces. The surface area of the
base is the area of a circle with a radius of about 8.2 cm. This area
is about 210 square cm. The surface area outside the base can be
computed as the approximate portion of the circular region used to form it.
Experimentally this can be determined by marking where the original circular
region overlaps to form the cone. The position can be calculated
theoretically by comparing the new radius (8.2 cm) to the old (10 cm).
The non base surface area is about 0.82 times the circular area $\pi 10^2$
which makes the area about 260 square cm. Adding 260 and 210 yields
the total surface area of 470 for the cone with maximal volume.

21 F.   One method is to use the grid to find the average radius. One
■   estimate is the average of 1, 1, 1, 11/12, 10/12, 8/12, 5/12,
        4/12, 6/12, 7/12 and 7/12 which is 11/16. The volume is then
the average cross sectional area which is $\pi(11/16)^2$ times the height, 2.
This yields the estimate of about 3 cu in for the volume.

22 A.   If X is the given triangle and Y is one of the seven triangles
■   shown below then the ratios are: I:X = $1/\sqrt{2} \sim 0.7$; II:X = $2/\sqrt{2} \sim$
        1.4; III:X = $\sqrt{5}/\sqrt{2} \sim 1.5$; IV:X = $\sqrt{10}/\sqrt{2} \sim 2.2$; V:X = $3/\sqrt{2} \sim 2.1$;
VI:X = $4/\sqrt{2} \sim 2.8$; VII:X = $2\sqrt{2}/\sqrt{2} = 2$. There are two additional triangles obtained from a six by six geoboard. The ratios are $\sqrt{17}/\sqrt{2}$
and $5/\sqrt{2}$. There are four additional triangles obtained from a seven by
seven geoboard. The ratios are $6/\sqrt{2}$, $3\sqrt{2}/\sqrt{2}$, $2\sqrt{5}/\sqrt{2}$ and $\sqrt{26}/\sqrt{2}$.

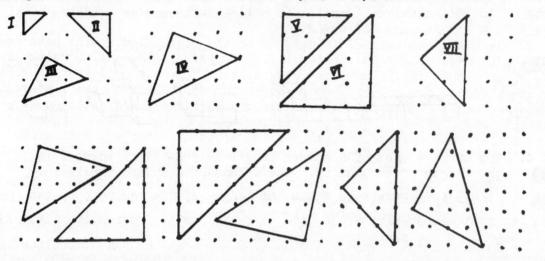

22 B.   Three quadrominoes have the similarity packing property. They are
■   the square, the rectangle and the L shape. The other two do not
        have the property. However the T shaped quadromino has the
property that $(4n)^2$ copies can be packed to make a similar quadromino
with scalar multiplier 4n. There are two pentominoes that have the
property. One is the 1 by 5 rectangle. The other is made by adjoining
a square to a square quadromino. To discover similarity packings it
is helpful to draw the similar pentomino first and then pack it with
copies of the smaller one.

22 C.   If area MNO:area MXY = 2:1 then MN:MX = $\sqrt{2}$:1. So we locate X on
■   MN so the ratio is as desired. We know the ratio of the diagonal
        of a square to its edge is $\sqrt{2}$:1. So construct any square ABCD and
its diagonal AC. Using the general strategy of Section 22.4 construct a
square similar to ABCD with diagonal MN. An edge of this square gives
the desired length MX. The second task requires that segments in the
ratio $\sqrt{3}$:1 be constructed. We know that the diagonal of a 1 by 2 rectangle
is $\sqrt{3}$. So we construct any 1 by 2 rectangle and its diagonal. Then construct a rectangle similar to it having diagonal MN. The shorter edge
of the rectangle gives the desired length MV. The third task is equivalent
to dividing trapezoid VNOW into equal areas by a segment ST parallel to
the bases VW and NO. But if area VSTW:area VNOW = 1:2 then VS:VN = 1:$\sqrt{2}$.
So we are back to the first task. We locate S on VN by constructing a

square with diagonal VN. The edge of the square has length VS.

22 D. ◼ Case 1 represents sufficient data to determine the similarity of the triangles. The given angle is between the edges whose lengths are proportional. The proportion determines the vertices D' and F' as endpoints of segments of known length. Case 2 also determines similar triangles. Since the sum of the three angles is constant, knowledge of the size of any two angles determines the size of the third. So in case 2 the third angles are also congruent. For two triangles three angles of one congruent to three angles of the other implies the triangles are similar. Case 3 is not sufficient to imply similarity of the triangles. There may be two locations for the vertex D'. In one location the triangles are similar; in the other location they are not. In the latter case FD and F'D' are not in the proper ratio.

22 E. ◼ Geoboard quadrilaterals similar to the given figure will have one of these scalar multipliers: 1, 2 or $\sqrt{2}$. If the scalar multiplier is 1 then the figures are congruent. There are 64 different positions on the geoboard for quadrilaterals congruent to the given quadrilateral. There are eight figures similar to the given quadrilateral with scalar multiplier 2. There are sixteen figures similar to the given figure with scalar multiplier $\sqrt{2}$. This problem helps students see similarity as being conserved by translations, rotations and reflections.

22 F. ◼ Some of the potential list where any two of the type are similar: segments, half-lines, lines, half-planes, circles, regular n-gons, cubes and other regular polyhedra, spheres.

22 G. ◼ One similarity class contains A, D, E, G and H. Any two kites in that class are similar to each other. Another similarity class is B, C, J and K. Any two kites in that class are similar to each other. The remaining kite F is in a class by itself. The following table gives the scalar multipliers as ratios.

A:D = 1:2	D:E = 1: $\sqrt{2}$	E:H = 2: $\sqrt{5}$	B:K = 1:2
A:E = 1:$\sqrt{2}$	D:G = 2:$\sqrt{5}$	G:H = 1:$\sqrt{2}$	C:J = $\sqrt{2}$:2
A:G = 1:$\sqrt{5}$	D:H = 2:$\sqrt{10}$	B:C = 1:1	C:K = 1:2
A:H = 1:$\sqrt{10}$	E:G = 2$\sqrt{2}$:$\sqrt{5}$	B:J = $\sqrt{2}$:2	J:K = 1:$\sqrt{2}$

All of the kites have one right angle. Getting any other angle of one kite congruent to a corresponding angle in another kite is sufficient to ensure similarity. Congruent angles can be found with the aid of tangent ratios using the lattice. Another strategy is to look at the ratio in which the shorter diagonal divides the longer diagonal. Finally there are other visual clues. For example A can be embedded in a square with the right angle of the kite A as an angle of the square. What other kites have this property?

23 A. ◼ First partition the set of pentagons into classes where the corresponding sides are parallel and oriented the same. There are three classes: 1) A, B, C, F; 2) D, E, J; 3) G, H, K. Now check within classes for central similarity. Since the check involves physical construction of lines, answers are approximate and may be subject to some

83.

disagreement. In the first class A and F are centrally similar and B and C are centrally similar. (A:F = 3:2 and B:C = 2:1). In the second class D and E are centrally similar and J and E are centrally similar. (D:E = 1:2 and J:E = 1:2). In the third class each is centrally similar to the other two. (G:K = 7:10 and H:K = 1:4 and G:H = 14:5).

23 B. Any geoboard segment parallel to FG but not congruent to it will ■ be centrally similar to FG. There are 30 such segments, 15 of length two, 10 of length three and 5 of length four. Seven of the segments that are centrally similar to FG have centers of similarity which are geoboard points. A is the center for similarity of FG with LN, QT and VZ. L is the center for similrity of FG with AC. F is the center for similarity of FG with FH, FJ and FK. Any geoboard segment parallel to LG but not congruent to it is centrally similar to LG. There are fourteen such segments, 9 have length $2\sqrt{2}$, 4 have length $3\sqrt{2}$ and one has length $4\sqrt{2}$. Four of the segments that are centrally similar to LG have centers of similarity which are geoboard points. A is the center for LG and VN; F is the center for LG and QH as well as the center for LG and VJ; L is the center for LG and LC. Any geoboard segment parallel to RO but not congruent to it will be centrally similar to RO. There are three such segments. N is the center of similarity for RO and VP, S is the center of similarity for RO and QK, X is the center for RO and LE. Each scaler multiplier is 2.

23 C. The figures $C_{Q,5/3}(P)$ and $C_{0,5/3}(P)$ must be translation congruent. ■ They must be congruent because they are both similar to P with the same scalar multiplier. They must be translation congruent because corresponding sides must be parallel. To characterize the vector for the translation consider centers Q and O and let X be a point of figure P. Let the length of QX be m, the length of OX be n and the length of QO be t. Suppose we find the figures centrally similar to P using both Q and O as centers and scalar multiplier k. Now follow point X. By definition the distance from X to $C_{0,k}(X)$ is (k-1)n. Similarly the distance from X to $C_{Q,k}(X)$ is (k-1)m. Further the angles QXO and $C_{0,k}(X) \, X \, C_{Q,k}(X)$ are congruent so triangle QXO is similar to triangle $C_{Q,k}(X) \, X \, C_{0,k}(X)$ with scalar multiplier k-1. So the length of $C_{0,k}(X) \, C_{Q,k}(X)$ is (k-1)t. So the translation vector which takes $C_{0,k}(P)$ to $C_{Q,k}(P)$ is parallel to QO and has length which is k-1 times QO.

23 D. The average area is computed as follows:

height	area
1/8	1/64 A
3/8	9/64 A
5/8	25/64 A
7/8	49/64 A

Average = $\frac{1}{4}$A (1 + 9 + 25 + 49)/64

= 21/64 A

~ 0.328 A

In the second case the average area is 1/8 A (1/256 + 9/256 + 25/256 + 49/256 + 81/256 + 121/256 + 169/256 + 225/256) = (1/8)(680/256)A ~ 0.332 A.

84.

23 E.   A composition of the type CR can make X coincide with Y. Since
■   X and Y have the same orientation no composition involving a
         single reflection will work. The transformation type CT will not
work because no translation can move X to where its sides will be parallel
to corresponding sides of Y. A rotation of 1/8 th clockwise turn (about
any turn center) will move X to have sides parallel to Y. Then an
appropriate central similarity can match them. To discuss X and Z next.
First note that they have opposite orientation so any composition which
matches them must contain a reflection. That eliminates CT and CR
as potential transformations to make X coincide with Z. Clearly a
composition of the type CЯR form will work. For example X can be rotated
(about any turn center) so that the bottom of boot X is parallel to the
bottom of boot Z. Then you can reflect in a line perpendicular to the
bottoms lines and have figures which are centrally similar. The job can
also be accomplished by a composition like CЯ if the reflection line is
chosen properly. To find a reflection line draw a line parallel to the
bottom of boot X, then a line parallel to the bottom of boot Z. One of
the angle bisectors of this pair of intersecting lines will be a reflection
line which will move X so that its edges are parallel to corresponding edges
of Z.

23 F.   If two circles are not congruent they must be centrally similar.
■   The center for a similarity is unique and is always collinear
         with the centers of the circles (because the similarity makes the
centers correspond). The rest of the discussion will assume that the two
circles being considered are not congruent. If circles are concentric
the center of similarity is the common center. If circles are tangent
with one in the interior of the other the center of similarity is the
point of tangency. If the circles intersect in two points or if the
circles are tangent but have no common interior points or if the circles
are disjoint then the center of similarity is exterior to both circles.
The center can be found by drawing radii in the same half-plane determined
by the line of centers perpendicular to the line of centers. The center
of similarity must be collinear with the outer endpoints of these radii.
If one circle is contained within the other the center of similarity will
be interior to the inner circle. The center can be found by the method
described above. You should expect all spheres which are not congruent
to be centrally similar.

23 G.   If the cone is sliced into two equal volumes then the volume ratio
■   of the top cone to the full cone is 1:2. The volume ratio is the
         cube of the length ratios. So the ratio of heights is $1:\sqrt[3]{2}$. This
ratio is about 4:5. (Note that $4^3 = 64$ and $5^3 = 125$ and $64:125 \sim 1:2$). So
you must slice the cone about 4/5th of the way from the top to divide it
intotwo equal volumes. If the cone is sliced into three equal volumes
then the ratio of the volume of the top cone to the volume of the full
cone is 1:3. That makes the ratio of heights $1:\sqrt[3]{3}$. This ratio is
about 7:10. (Note $7^3 = 343$ and $10^3 = 1000$ and $343:1000 \sim 1:3$). So you must
make the first slice about 7/10 ths of the way from the top. The second
slice has the ratio of volumes at 2:3 so the height ratio is $\sqrt[3]{2} : \sqrt[3]{3}$.
This ratio is about 7/8. The second cut should be made about 7/8 of the
way from the top.

24 A. The relation is $P_A = 2eP_e$. The relation can be deduced from these tables.

P_e	interval e	interval A	P_A	
2	(6,8)	(36,64)	28	
$\frac{1}{2}$	(6 3/4, 7 1/4)	(45 9/16, 52 9/16)	7	when
3	(5 1/2, 8 1/2)	(30 1/4, 72 1/4)	42	$e = 7$
$\frac{1}{4}$	(6 7/8, 7 1/8)	(47 17/64, 50 49/64)	$3\frac{1}{2}$	
$2\frac{1}{2}$	(5 3/4, 8 1/4)	(33 1/16, 68 1/16)	35	
2	(9, 11)	(81, 121)	40	
$\frac{1}{2}$	(9 3/4, 11 1/4)	(95 1/16, 105 1/16)	10	when
3	(8 1/2, 11 1/2)	(72 1/4, 132 1/4)	60	$e = 10$
$\frac{1}{4}$	(9 7/8, 10 1/8)	(97 33/64, 102 33/64)	5	
$2\frac{1}{2}$	(8 3/4, 11 1/4)	(76 7/16, 126 7/16)	50	

Note that the interval for e is $(e-\frac{1}{2}P_e, \; e+\frac{1}{2}P_e)$. When $s = 6e^2$ then the interval for S is $(6e^2-6eP_e + 3/2\,P_e^2, \; 6e^2+6eP_e+3/2\,P_e^2)$. Hence $P_S = 12eP_e$. The precision unit for volume of a cube is $(e+\frac{1}{2}P_e)^3 - (e-\frac{1}{2}P_e)^3 = 3e^2P_e + \frac{1}{4}P_e^3$. When P_e is small then $\frac{1}{4}P_e^3$ is considerably smaller and the precision unit is close to $3e^2P_e$.

24 B. The relative error is given by $(u-\ell)/(u+\ell)$. The accuracy index is 1-relative error so the accuracy index is $2\ell/(u+\ell)$. The relative error has a least value of zero when $u = \ell$. This occurs if the measurement is exact. In real circumstances this would not occur. The greatest relative error is 1 and it occurs when $\ell = 0$. If $\ell > 0$ then the relative error is between zero and one. The least accuracy index is zero and occurs when $\ell = 0$. The greatest accuracy index is 1 and occurs when $u = \ell$, ie when measurement is exact.

24 C. There is only one geoboard triangle which has a precision unit of one. It is possible to find three geoboard n-gons which have precision unit one for all n greater than or equal to 4. It becomes easier to find examples as n gets larger. (If n got too large it would again become impossible because of the size restriction of the board.) The figures constructed must be the union of a polyomino and a single half-square. Examples follow.

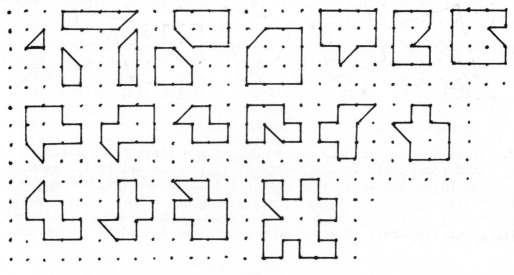

24 D. There is good practice with inner and outer measure that can be
accomplished with this problem. Triangles with precision units which
are whole numbers from 1 to 12 inclusive have been found. The
pictures appear below.

24 E. Using the average of the inner and outer measures as estimate
the precision unit is the difference between the inner and outer
measures. The precision unit can be as small as zero when the
inner and outer measures are the same. This happens for polyominoes. For
a 5 by 5 geoboard the maximum precision unit is sixteen and occurs when
the outer measure is sixteen and the inner measure is zero. For geoboard
triangles the minimum precision unit is 1. A right triangle which is half
of a geoboard square has inner measure zero and outer measure one. The
maximum precision unit is twelve. An example is given which has an
inner measure of 1 and an outer measure of 13. For quadrilaterals the
minimum may be zero because a quadrilateral could be a polyomino. The
maximum precision unit for a quadrilateral is twelve. An example of a
square having inner measure 4 and outer measure 16 is given. Another
example having outer and inner measures of 15 and 3 respectively is
given. For geoboard pentagons the smallest precision unit is one; the
greatest is sixteen. For polygons with an even number of edges the
minimum precision unit is zero; for polygons with an odd number of edges
the minimum precision unit is one. For polygons with five or more edges
the maximum precision unit is sixteen.

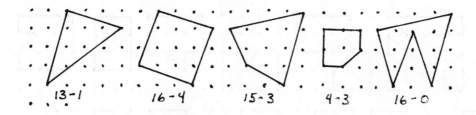

13-1   16-4   15-3   4-3   16-0

24 F. There are two methods for determining a "best approximation" that
students suggest. One method is to use the arithmetic mean of
the given measures. The other is to find the average of the
greatest and least of the given measures. The precision unit could
be determined by taking the difference between the greatest and least
of the given measures. However as new measures are added to the pool

an awareness developes that the bounds are not absolute. There may be more extreme measures that are the results of other attempts. This motivates the idea of a confidence interval. Rather than say "4 to the nearest tenth" and mean "I am 100% confident that the true measure is in the interval from 3.95 to 4.05" one might use an interval in which there is less confidence. One might say " I am 95% confident that the true measure is in the interval from 9.1 to 9.2". The 95% figure could be the result of examining the estimates and noting that 95% of them are in that interval.

24 G. ■ In this problem it is necessary to use the relationship between accuracy index and GPE and the relationship between GPE and precision unit for measuring length. When the accuracy index is 0.8 then $0.8 = 1 - GPE/\ell$ where ℓ is the length of the page. That means $GPE = 0.2\,\ell$. Since GPE is half the precision unit, the precision unit is $0.4\,\ell$. Consequently in order to measure the page you need a ruler whose consecutive marks are separated by a distance of $0.4\,\ell$. Similar reasoning applies to other accuracy indices. In order to measure ℓ with accuracy index 0.9 you need a ruler with consecutive marks that are $0.2\,\ell$ apart. If the accuracy index is to be 0.95 the distance between consecutive marks must be $0.1\,\ell$. An accuracy index of 1 would be impossible since it would require a rular whose consecutive marks would be $0 \cdot \ell$ apart. There would be no distance between consecutive marks!